THE
NATURAL ESTROGEN
BOOK

THE
NATURAL ESTROGEN
BOOK

A natural treatment for the symptoms of menopause
which provides healthy eating for the whole family

DR LANA LIEW

THE NATURAL ESTROGEN BOOK

First published in Australasia in 1998 by
Simon & Schuster Australia
20 Barcoo Street, East Roseville NSW 2069

A Viacom Company
Sydney New York London Toronto Tokyo Singapore

Reprinted in 1998

Text © Dr L. Liew 1998
Illustrations © Katie Jordan 1998

National Library of Australia
Cataloguing-in-Publication data

Liew, Lana.
The natural estrogen book : a natural treatment for the
symptoms of menopause which provides healthy eating
for the whole family.

Includes index.
ISBN 0 7318 0702 2.

1. Menopause - Hormone therapy. 2. Menopause -
Complications - Diet therapy - Recipes. 3. Menopause -
Nutritional aspects. I. Title.

618.1750654

Cover art: Katie Jordan
Cover design: Anna Soo
Internal design and illustrations: Katie Jordan
Photography: Matthew Waters
Printed in Australia by Australian Print Group

FOREWORD

The latest focus in nutrition research is on phytoestrogens. Phytoestrogens are a diverse group of plant-derived substances which have estrogenic activity in animals. These compounds are similar to estrogens and are characterised by their ability to illicit a specific response in estrogen sensitive tissues. There is a great deal of interest in the potential benefits of dietary phytoestrogens in hormone-dependent processes. Animals have been known to graze selectively on plants to enhance or diminish fertility. Much of the early research on phytoestrogens was done with animals and interest was induced by the observation that sheep who grazed too much on clover became infertile. Epidemiological studies have shown that the incidence of hormone-dependent diseases is significantly lower in Asian populations whose diets are high in phytoestrogen consumption. Further studies comparing Asian native women to other cultures have suggested that the high phytoestrogen content of their diets may be responsible in part for their low rate of breast cancer and the ease with which they pass through the menopause.

Phytoestrogens have both weak estrogenic and anti-estrogenic activity. Estradiol, our bodies' strongest estrogen, can be released from the ovary and travel to any number of target tissues, including the breast and uterus. At the breast, the estradiol can bind to the receptor site and increase cell division; at the uterus, estradiol can cause the endometrial lining to thicken. However, not all substances have a positive effect on the target tissue. Such is the case with Tamoxifen, a drug which is used in the treatment of breast cancer. Tamoxifen can bind to the estrogen receptors of the breast without causing any increase in cell division, thereby acting as an 'estrogen blocker'. At the same time, it can bind to receptors in the uterus and cause proliferation of the endometrium. Tamoxifen therefore has an anti-estrogenic effect on the breast, but a pro-estrogenic effect on the uterus.

The most commonly studied phytoestrogens include the isoflavonoids, lignans and coumestans found in high amounts in soybeans, flaxseed and alfalfa, and also in many other vegetables and fruits. Much of the original research was targeted at menopausal women. Phytoestrogens have an estrogenic effect on the vaginal epithelium similar to that seen in patients treated with hormone replacement therapy. There is evidence, too, that hot flushes are resolved. Phytoestrogens also exert a cardiovascular protective effect by regulating lipid levels. Dietary soy supplementation has been shown to increase bone mineral density. Phytoestrogens may also protect against some types of cancer. Finally, there is evidence that there is a lower incidence of breast, colon and prostate cancer in Asia, where soy intake is high in comparison to Western countries, where intake is relatively low.

Certainly, more studies of women using phytoestrogens need to be done to establish both the benefits and risks. However, given the bulk of information available, the use of phytoestrogen in a well-balanced diet may be considered a relatively safe method of effecting estrogen activity.

Dr Randall E. Fray, M.B., Ch.B., F.R.C.O.G., F.R.A.C.O.G.
Gynaecologist
Bankstown

CONTENTS

ACKNOWLEDGMENTS

Many scientists throughout the world have worked tirelessly in the research of phytoestrogen-containing foods and their effects on the health of men and women. They are too numerous to name, but each and every one of them has contributed to the knowledge from which this book draws — the research into disease prevention using pure extracts of isoflavones and other plant products.

My eldest daughter, Camilla, was most enthusiastic about this book and she spurred me on with it. Her encouragement and support are most appreciated, not to mention her help with research, proofreading and tasting of the recipes.

I would also like to thank my two younger daughters, who understood that their time with their mother had to be shared with a compelling project. They, too, have been most patient and supportive.

Special thanks are due to the following friends: Margaret, Bev, Nanny, Annie, Siew Fong, Stephanie and Christopher, who have shared their recipes, thoughts and interest. Above all, their belief and support have been vital in the development of this book. Many patients have also encouraged me along the way.

Acknowledgments of help are also due to the following: Dora Spilbergs for proofreading and useful comments; Evan Black for help with some research articles; Grahame and Lyndall Black for sustaining encouragement and interest; Jenny Chan, Consultant Dietitian-Nutritionist (B.Sc., Masters in Nutrition and Dietetics, MDAA, APD), for her work and contribution to the analysis of the recipes; Dr Randall Fray for his interest and enthusiasm in the book; Professor John Eden for his helpful suggestions and comments; and David Rosenberg, Brigitta Doyle and Siobhan O'Connor at Simon & Schuster for their assistance in the production of this book.

INTRODUCTION

Hormone replacement therapy (HRT) is a popular discussion topic amongst women in the peri-menopausal and menopausal age groups. Many women are happy with their HRT and should continue on the therapy as supervised by their doctors. However, there are women who have tried HRT in various combinations and forms to their disappointment because of the numerous undesirable side-effects. There are also those for whom HRT is a definite contraindication.

Many women have expressed an interest in using natural ways of controlling their menopausal symptoms. Although some women have knowledge of the estrogen food list, they are often frustrated by the lack of guidance regarding how to utilise the ingredients in everyday living.

This book uses foods rich in naturally occurring plant estrogens to boost the daily intake. The overwhelming majority of the recipes are very healthy, with low cholesterol content. At least 55 recipes use soy products that contain the most potent of a subclass of plant estrogens. However, as plant estrogens are very weak compared to the estrogens in HRT, a quite substantial quantity of specific foods needs to be ingested in order to keep up the beneficial effects.

Research has shown the various benefits of plant estrogens, in particular, soy products. Not only does soy benefit women, but it is also beneficial to men. Reduction in coronary heart disease rates, blood pressure and cholesterol have all been demonstrated with soy ingestion in human subjects. Two soy units per day are required for this effect, preferably in divided doses — i.e. one soy unit in the morning and one at night. Soy consumption is also associated with lower rates of prostate cancer and bowel cancer in men.

Menopausal women, on the other hand, will probably need 4 to 5 soy units per day if they are using soy as an alternative to HRT. Some women have reported control of their menopausal symptoms with as little as 2 soy units per day. Again, the soy units should be taken in divided doses. Maximum effect may not be felt until 4 to 8 weeks after commencement of the diet. Also, it may be difficult for some women to ingest the suggested amount of soy units. Food supplements using various ingredients such as red clover and concentrated soy protein isolates are now being marketed by various companies to supply the demand for a 'natural' approach to the relief of menopausal symptoms.

When changing over to soy milk from cow's milk, it may be easier for some people to start by drinking flavoured soy milk, or alternatively mixing half soy milk with half cow's milk and gradually increasing the proportion of soy milk until full strength.

There are some humans who are non-responders, i.e. they are not able to absorb the plant estrogens for various reasons. Persisting with the diet in non-responders is useless. Also, those who may be allergic to soy or legumes should avoid the diet as the products are likely to aggravate their allergies.

Chapter Three deals with soy products. Many readers may not have seen these products, let alone tasted them. Photographs of some commonly used soy products can be found on pages 140–143. Readers can use the pictures to indicate to storekeepers what they intend to purchase, especially when they visit an Asian store where the salesperson is not fluent in the reader's native language.

In Chapter Four, soy unit exchanges are given to guide you towards the quantity you will need to eat. Eating excessive amounts will not necessarily benefit you. A soy unit exchange is a bit like the concept of carbohydrate exchange in the diet of a diabetic. In the current research papers, a soy meal (unit) refers to 1 cup (250 mL, 8 fl oz) soy milk, but there are other products that can be used in exchange for the same amount of plant estrogens present in that 1 cup of soy milk. It will be easy to follow. Alternatively, the soy unit content of the recipes containing soy will give readers a guide as to the number of soy units they are cooking. Divide the total soy units in the recipe by the number of servings from the recipe and you will get the net soy unit for that particular food and serving size.

The total energy, cholesterol and calcium contents are given for each recipe rather than for each serving as serving size is not standard. To benefit from the information, divide the values given for each recipe by the number of servings you obtain, especially if you are watching your weight and cholesterol levels.

I wish my readers good luck with their cooking and many years of good health, delight and enjoyment of the natural estrogen diet.

PART I

❖

NATURAL
ESTROGENS

CHAPTER ONE

ESTROGEN FOODS
AND MENOPAUSE

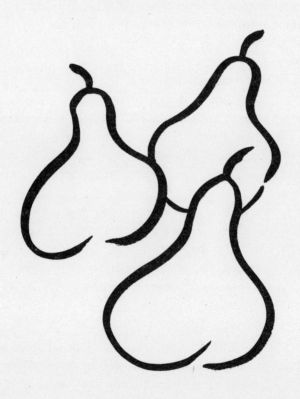

MENOPAUSE AND HORMONE REPLACEMENT THERAPY

Every woman (if she lives long enough) will eventually go through menopause. Some women will sail through this phase of their lives without any problems, while a significant number will require medical help with the various complaints associated with the menopause.

Hot flushes are a major symptom of the menopause affecting some 60 to 80 per cent of women in the menopausal age groups in Western society (this percentage is much less in Eastern countries). This symptom can be mild to severe and differs from woman to woman in its severity. Hormones are usually prescribed to control hot flushes and other unpleasant symptoms of the menopause. Those who are prescribed hormone replacement therapy (HRT) and feel good whilst on it should stay on it under the supervision of their doctors. HRT does offer benefits in osteoporosis prevention and lower the risks of heart attacks and strokes in the long term. Recent research suggests that estrogens also benefit brain function and may be used in the prevention and treatment of Alzheimer's disease in women.

There are some women, however, who are unable to tolerate HRT in any form and, after giving up HRT, turn to alternative treatments. Another group of women simply cannot take HRT because it is contraindicated. This group consists of women who suffer from breast cancer, ovarian cancer or uterine cancer. They, too, can suffer from menopausal symptoms and are in need of alternative measures to help them cope with their symptoms.

At the time of writing, some menopause clinics are conducting trials of HRT in selected women who in the past had breast cancers treated with chemotherapy or radiotherapy. Unless we are very sure that HRT does not increase the recurrence rate of breast cancer, a lot of doctors will be advising their patients to avoid it or prescribe it only with written informed consent from the patient.

WHAT ARE OTHER SYMPTOMS OF THE MENOPAUSE?

Some women would have heard from older friends, relatives and their mothers about some of the complaints they experienced during menopause. Others may have read about it in women's magazines or newspapers, or heard about it in health seminars, on the radio or on television shows.

When the ovaries age, or when they are removed in an operation, the female hormones that keep the female body and brain functioning are no longer produced in the same quantity as before. In the absence of adequate quantities of estrogens, a woman may start to experience some of the following symptoms:

❖ anxiety
❖ backache
❖ depression
❖ discomfort or pain during intercourse (dyspareunia)
❖ dry skin
❖ dry vagina
❖ headaches
❖ hot flushes
❖ increased facial hair
❖ insomnia (difficulty sleeping)
❖ irritability
❖ itchy skin, as if insects are crawling about (formication)
❖ joint aches
❖ lack of sexual drive (loss of libido)
❖ light-headedness
❖ loss of concentration
❖ mood swings
❖ muscle aches
❖ poor memory
❖ tiredness
❖ urinary stress incontinence

Menopausal symptoms can start a few years before the periods stop all together. The actual time designated for menopause is really the last period, but this is a retrospective label as the periods should have ceased for 12 months before one is said to have gone through the menopause. In other words, if your periods have stopped coming for one whole year, then you are considered to have experienced menopause.

Periods can be irregular or heavy a few years prior to the menopause. In general, the time when all these irregularities and complaints of menopausal symptoms start to happen until the periods actually stop can take four or five years. The average age of menopause is around 50 years of age, with the range between 35 to 59 years.

PHYTOESTROGENS AND ALTERNATIVE MEASURES

The soybean is known to contain phytoestrogens (plant estrogens), which are quite effective in controlling menopausal symptoms in Asian women. Although classified as a weak estrogen, the phytoestrogen by-products have been found to be excreted in significant amounts in the urine of Asian men and women. It has been postulated that the estrogens from plant sources bind to the estrogen receptor sites within the body, thus reducing the effects of a low-estrogen state such as seen in menopause.

Soy and other foods have been widely recognised as an 'alternative natural management' for the hot flushes of menopause.

Clonidine, a drug marketed by Boehringer Ingelheim, can be added to an estrogen diet in doses of 25 mcg two or three times per day to obtain better control of hot flushes in some women who are still suffering from them. This drug requires prescription from a registered medical practitioner. Some researchers do not feel that it should be used alone for the treatment of menopausal symptoms. It is certainly not the same as HRT.

Herbal medicines such as *Panax ginseng*, *Angelica sinensis* (dong quai), *Dioscorea opposita*/*Dioscorea villosa*, lime flowers, cimicifuga and *Salvia officinalis* are some of the measures used by herbalists to treat menopausal symptoms. Although these can be easily obtained across the counter, self-medication is not recommended, as titration of the doses is a rather tricky art. A reputable registered herbalist should be consulted about the usage and dosage for each individual case. The margin of safety in dosing is narrow.

Trials in Melbourne to test the efficacy of Chinese herbs in the treatment of menopausal symptoms are under way. We await with interest the results of this much-needed and scientifically structured research project.

At present, there is no answer to the question: How much phytoestrogen food is enough? Research in menopausal women using these foods is being conducted in order to determine the amount required by the female body during the deficiency state.

Different individuals differ in their metabolism and absorption of any food or medication. This is also applicable to estrogen foods. Two women experiencing the same amount of hot flushes and menopausal symptoms ratings can eat the same amount of estrogen foods, yet have different levels of relief from their symptoms.

Looking at the Asian and, in particular, Japanese diet, one can see that large amounts of soy and plant products which are also rich in phytoestrogens are consumed, while fat consumption is very low. Urinary excretion of the by-products is at least 10 to 100 times more than that of Caucasians. Studies on the incidence of breast, colon and prostate cancers among Asians and Caucasians have suggested that the incidence of these cancers is linked to diet, as migrant Asian populations adopting a Western diet — high in fats and low in vegetables and fibre — have a much higher incidence of these cancers than the population in their homelands.

It has been estimated that the daily Asian diet may contain up to 50 g (2 oz) of soy proteins, as well as a significant amount of legumes, cereals and grains rich in estrogens. Most experiments or trials use pure extracts of a particular isoflavone, but some studies have used or are using soy flour or soy products to assess the effects of these products on blood pressure, cholesterol, hot flushes and other biochemical and vaginal cell changes. Recently, a 40 per cent reduction in hot flushes was demonstrated in a study using soy flour conducted in Melbourne.

Some foods contain more potent phytoestrogens than others. Studies have shown soy, rye, linseed, clover and chickpeas (garbanzo beans) to contain effective phytoestrogens. The foods listed on page 21 contain one or more of the phytoestrogens groups, namely isoflavones, lignans and coumestans. This list is by no means complete as further research is being carried out all the time.

Isoflavones can be subdivided into daidzein, genistein, daidzin, genistin, formononetin, biochanin A and others. Of these, genistein is the most powerful and most talked about amongst the food scientists. Studies are been conducted to study the many uses of genistein and especially its role in cancer therapy. It is hoped that genistein extracted from soybeans may be released for controlled use in the near future.

Soy is rather new to Western cuisine and the question 'How do I eat soy?' is probably a very common response when a woman is told to eat more soy by her doctor or gynaecologist. Apart from containing potent phytoestrogens, the soybean also contains other beneficial chemicals such as amino acids, protease inhibitors and phytic acids. It contains all the eight essential amino acids present in meat proteins, thus making soy a first-class protein food. Now that the scientific world has been alerted to its many healthful properties, studies are being designed and carried out into this humble bean which has been cultivated for several thousand years.

WHAT ARE SOME OF THE PROPERTIES OF THE ISOFLAVONES?

Apart from being natural, isoflavones have antibacterial, antiviral and antifungal properties. They also contain anti-inflammatory, anti-oxidative and anti-angiogenic agents. The latter property prevents new blood vessel formation and therefore restricts the growth of tumours which depend on blood-bringing nutrients to feed their high metabolism.

Recent studies have also shown isoflavones to have bone-density preservation properties, although these are not as good as those in natural estrogens present in HRT.

Isoflavones have antihypertensive properties, so that blood pressure can be decreased in the long term. This works through the smooth muscle relaxation effects of isoflavone on the blood vessel walls, lowering of the low density lipoprotein (LDL) and total cholesterol.

FACTORS AFFECTING THE NATURAL PHYTOESTROGENS

❖ The season in which a plant is harvested is important in determining its plant estrogen content. Asians have traditionally been fussy about the timing of the harvest of plant and animal products. This knowledge is passed on from generation to generation without a scientific explanation. It is now known that the concentrations of phytoestrogens vary with the maturity of the plant and the timing of the harvesting.

❖ The genetic origin of the plant and climatic and environmental effects on the plant during its growth will also affect the phyto-estrogens.

❖ The degree to which the product is processed has been found to affect plant estrogens in that the phytoestrogen content diminishes with further processing.

❖ The presence of appropriate bacteria in the intestines of the consumer is important for the digestion and facilitation of the absorption of phytoestrogens.

❖ The transit time of the plant product in the intestines determines how much phytoestrogen can be absorbed. Absorption depends on a normal and efficient gastrointestinal system.

WHAT ARE THE ADVANTAGES OF THE NATURAL ESTROGEN DIET?

❖ It is natural. It occurs naturally in foods, fruits and herbs. The presence of other compounds in the foods which we use in our daily living tend to neutralise to a certain extent the possible side-effects of a specific food. For example, the pectin present in apples will neutralise the constipating effects of ginger or sesame oil.

❖ These foods are readily available and do not require prescriptions or a visit to a health practitioner at regular intervals.

❖ These estrogens are present in healthy foods, as you can judge from the list given on page 21.

❖ The foods contain other beneficial compounds such as anti-oxidants and natural vitamins.

❖ It can help prevent or lower risks of breast cancer, colon cancer and prostate cancer (in men).

❖ This type of treatment is less costly to the health system and to the patient. At present, government subsidies through the PBS for tablets and patches amount from a few dollars to hundreds of dollars per patient per year of treatment on HRT.

❖ There is a psychological benefit. You are not taking medicines every day to stay young or in order to feel 'normal'.

❖ It is a weak estrogen. It therefore cannot exert any major side-effects such as nausea, fluid retention, headaches and so on which some women on HRT suffer.

❖ Most of these foods are high in fibre content and therefore aid bowel function.

WHAT ARE THE DISADVANTAGES OF THE NATURAL ESTROGEN DIET?

❖ There is no standardisation of doses. How much phytoestrogen is enough is still a research question, unlike with the conventional tablets or patches which come in standard doses (even though titration of doses is often required after a woman goes on the specific HRT).

❖ Following a diet is inconvenient for some people who rely on swallowing a tablet or slapping on a patch to remedy their problem.

❖ Certain foods or ingredients may be difficult to obtain or prepare.

❖ There is a lack of knowledge in the community of how to use the foods and their preparation.

❖ Effectiveness depends on both product factors and patient factors. As previously discussed, absorption of phytoestrogen depends on the intestinal transit time, the status of the gut, the presence of appropriate bacteria and the amount of chemicals in the plant product which is influenced by the genetic origin and the climatic and environmental conditions.

❖ It takes a few months before the patient starts to experience the benefits of the natural estrogen diet. It is therefore not as fast-acting as HRT.

❖ Some patients may experience flatulence (wind) during the early days of treatment.

The Estrogen Food List

Legumes
Alfalfa
Chickpeas (garbanzo beans)
Cowpeas (black-eyed peas)
Green or garden peas
Green, string or French beans
Lentils
Mung bean sprouts
Red beans (adzuki beans)
Red clover
Soybeans
Soy sprouts
Split or field peas

Oils
Corn oil
Olive oil
Sesame oil
Soybean oil
Sunflower oil

Vegetables
Beetroot (beet)
Cabbage
Carrots
Marrow
Pumpkin
Rhubarb
Squash

Spices and Herbs
Anise seed
Cloves
Garlic
Fennel
Licorice
Sage
Tea

Seeds
Linseed
Sesame
Sunflower

Fruits
Apples
Cherries
Grapes
Olives
Pears
Plums
Pomegranates
Prunes

Cereals/Grains
Barley
Corn
Oats
Rice
Rye
Wheat

CHAPTER TWO

THE HEALTH PLAN

The Health Plan

There is no need to eat the same foods every day. Have a variety to 'bring some spice into your life'. Make your meals interesting. Experiment with the foods in different combinations. Add to or substitute the ingredients in the recipes which you are currently using in your cooking: Who knows, you might come up with a really fantastic new recipe.

The nutritional guidelines are still applicable: eat less salt, less sugar and less fat. Eat more calcium-rich foods, fruits, vegetables and cereals.

❖ For menopausal women, a dietary intake of 1000 to 1500 mg of calcium is the current recommendation. The higher amount is for women with established osteoporosis.

❖ Exercise to keep your joints mobile and heart and lungs in good shape.

❖ In general, a minimum of 30 minutes of brisk walking three times per week will help you along the path of wellness. Current studies suggest that 5 hours per week of exercise is the optimal goal for maintenance of fitness.

❖ Have adequate sleep and rest.

❖ Remember to drink at least 6 glasses of water per day and try to avoid carbonated or soft drinks. Go easy on alcoholic drinks as well. Studies have shown excess alcoholic consumption (more than two standard drinks per 24 hours) is associated with increased risk of osteoporosis and also possibly an increase in the risk of breast cancer.

❖ Avoid smoking as much as you can and try to give it up if you smoke.

❖ Keep a check on your cholesterol levels and discuss any risk of osteoporosis with your doctor, especially if there is a family history of this problem.

❖ Have a positive attitude towards this phase of your life as you can help yourself more than others can.

❖ Perform self-examination of breasts monthly. The best time is straight after your periods if you are still menstruating. For those who do not have periods any more or have had a hysterectomy, the beginning of the month is just as good a time as any. Just pick a regular date that is easy for you to remember.

❖ If you are more than 50 years of age, present yourself for mammography screening every two years. In special circumstances, this may be altered by your health adviser to a yearly review, especially where there is a strong family history of breast cancer. When you find a breast lump, do not panic — make an appointment with your doctor to have it checked. Take along any old films of the breast that you have stored away in the cupboard.

❖ At present, the health department and its panel of expert advisers are encouraging women to have a pap smear every two years. Again, in special circumstances your doctor or gynaecologist may vary that schedule according to your past history or family history. No test is 100 per cent accurate. If symptoms of a worrying kind still persist after a check-up, return to your health adviser for a review after a few weeks rather than waiting for another year. Those women who have had a hysterectomy do not generally need to have a pap smear unless the surgery was performed for treatment of genital tract cancer. These women need close follow-up tests by their doctor or gynaecologist.

❖ Those women who have had a hysterectomy for other reasons, such as heavy bleeding, benign cysts, benign tumours or fibroids, will need an internal examination to check the ovaries when they visit their doctors for their yearly check-ups.

SOME GENERAL ADVICE REGARDING THE NATURAL ESTROGEN DIET

There are no official guidelines regarding natural estrogen intake in our daily diet, but the following pointers are based on current knowledge derived from decades of research by various dedicated food scientists. As new information becomes available in the future, official guidelines may be drawn up in the light of new, accepted standards. However, it may take another generation of scientists' work to steer us accurately into such a complicated maze.

❖ Consume at least two soy units per day. A soy unit is equivalent to 1–1¼ cups (250–300 mL, 8–10 fl oz) of soy milk. However, not every one will be keen to drink that amount of soy milk each day. On average, phytoestrogen content is approximately 1 mg per gram of soy protein. It actually varies between 0.5 to 3 mg per gram of soy protein as variations in genetic origin of the soy plants, season of harvest and climatic and environmental conditions are factors influencing the concentration of the phytoestrogens. Those who are worried about fat content of the milk can use the fat-reduced variety: defatting of soy products in general does not affect the phytoestrogen content significantly.

❖ Aim to consume a total of 30 to 50 mg of phytoestrogens per day in the selection of estrogen-rich foods. It is very hard to be accurate about the actual content in each foodstuff as natural estrogens vary with the variety, time of harvest, genetic origin and so on of the plant product and the amount of processing the food has undergone.

❖ Consuming excessive amounts such as four to five times the average Asian daily diet will not necessarily be beneficial as improvements in serum cholesterol, blood pressure, hot flushes and other menopausal symptoms do not bear a linear relationship to the dose. Flooding of all the estrogen receptor sites with excessive phytoestrogens may produce an anti-estrogenic response. So, eat in moderation.

❖ There is no need to eat the same foods every day. Other foods in the list and those not yet on the list also contain phytoestrogens. Their lower phytoestrogen content simply means a larger quantity has to be ingested to give the desired effects. In the Asian and Japanese diets, rice, barley and other grains, seeds, beans, legumes, sprouts, tea and seafood feature in every meal. All these contribute to the supply of plant estrogens.

❖ Broad spectrum antibiotics do kill the good bacteria in the bowel (gut), and therefore the plant estrogens may not be available for absorption despite eating adequate quantities of estrogen-rich foods. It may take two to six weeks for your system to recover after a course of antibiotics. Hence, when hot flushes and menopausal symptoms reappear, do not panic; it is only a temporary setback.

❖ Overindulgence in one particular foodstuff to the exclusion of other food groups can produce a pathological state. For example, a patient eating excessive amounts of carrots, pumpkin or corn can manifest carotenemia; in a young, menstruating female, this can cause the cessation of periods (amenorrhoea). However, on resuming a normal diet and excluding the offending excess food item for a few months, normal function will resume.

❖ Carbonated drinks and excessive phytic acids in some vegetables can chelate the calcium and therefore impair calcium absorption despite adequate intake on calculation. Calcium is optimally absorbed in the presence of vitamins C and D. The latter presents no problems if you are an outdoor person as you will absorb plenty of vitamin D through sunlight. This only becomes a problem when a woman is tucked away in a dark room with little exposure to sunlight. Yet one has to be sensible about sunlight exposure as skin does burn readily. Sunscreen protection should always be used to reduce ultraviolet (UV) light damage. Morning sun is better than midday sun, but it still can damage the skin with prolonged, unprotected exposures.

❖ Calcium is needed to build your bones. From the age of 30, we lose about 0.5 to 0.6 per cent of our bone density each year onwards. After the menopause, women's bone density loss accelerates in the absence of estrogens in the first five to 10 years of the post-menopause phase. Dietary phytoestrogens appear to help rectify this problem, but do not seem to be as efficient as HRT. Thin or osteoporotic bones are easily fractured with a minor fall or trauma.

❖ Excessive salt, alcohol and caffeine ingestion have been reported to have a negative impact on bone density. Calcium supplements when prescribed by the doctor are best taken at night on an empty stomach as food and plant fibre do interfere with their absorption from the gut.

❖ Women experiencing sore breasts during the diet should avoid foods and beverages containing caffeine as these tend to aggravate breast tenderness and lumpiness. Avoid foods containing high amounts of salicylates, such as tomatoes, oranges and pineapples, if the periods are heavy. Salicylates do thin the blood and aggravate the heavy flow. Resume your usual diet after a break of four or five days.

IS THE NATURAL ESTROGEN DIET FOR MENOPAUSAL WOMEN ONLY?

Although the natural estrogen diet is primarily aimed at peri-menopausal and menopausal women, its health benefits can be extended to men, children and other females. In general, 1 or 2 soy units for men, children and pre-menopausal females is adequate for cardiac and blood pressure benefits. In the adult male, the benefits also include lowering of the risk of prostate and bowel cancer. In the pre-menopausal woman, the added benefits are lowering of the risk of breast cancer and bowel cancer.

CHAPTER THREE

SOY PRODUCTS

There is a large variety of soy products in most supermarkets, Asian food stores and health food stores. More and more soy products are appearing on the shelves each month when you visit the food stores.

SOYBEANS

Soybeans belong to the legume family. The plant produces pods which, when matured, will contain two or three seeds in each pod. These seeds are the famous soybeans — sometimes called soya beans — which have been in use in China for several thousand years. In China, it was commonly known as wang tul or 'yellow bean'. The dried beans are a yellowish to creamy colour with a rather tough skin and slightly smaller in size than our green or garden peas. In the United States, you can find them in green, brown, black or speckled colours, as well as the common yellow soybeans. The commercial varieties are sold dried in packages.

SOY MILK AND SOY DRINKS

When you visit your supermarket, you can be sure to find a variety of brands of soy drinks on the shelves in UHT or long-life packs. They come in a variety of flavours and sizes, too. Fat and carbohydrate content varies from brand to brand. Try to drink about 2–2$\frac{1}{2}$ cups (600 mL, 20 fl oz) per day.

The energy content per serve will depend on whether or not it is a fat-reduced preparation. A comparison of the contents of the various brands can be found on page 32.

You can make your own fresh soy drinks from soybeans purchased from the supermarket or Asian food stores. A recipe for this is found on page 50.

Health food stores and Asian food stores do carry fresh soy drinks or 'soy milk' in refrigerated form, usually in 1-litre (1-quart) or 2-litre (2-quart) plastic containers. More recently, supermarkets are carrying fresh packs of soy milk in their dairy sections.

Powdered soy formula for babies has been available for more than 15 years in Australia. I am sure some readers are familiar with names such as Prosobee, Isomil and Infasoy. There are also powdered soy drinks in individual sachets for travelling convenience if you ask at the Asian food stores. The powdered soy drink (unsuitable for infant feeding) can be reconstituted with hot water. This tastes rather sweet as it contains added sugar. You can leave it to cool or add cold water or ice cubes after reconstituting with a smaller quantity of hot water. Carnation soy drink powder is available in some supermarkets. A packet makes 2.5 litres ($2^1/_2$ quarts) of soy drink.

One develops a taste for soy drink with time. Most patients have told me it is hard to change over from cow's milk initially. Those who do certainly appreciate the fact that soy milk is cholesterol-free. If you have trouble changing over to soy milk, do it gradually by mixing a portion of the soy milk with your usual milk, and increasing the proportion with time.

There has been a lot of interest in the cholesterol-lowering effect of soy, its prostate cancer reduction properties and, more recently, the reduction of hot flushes and breast cancer protection effects of this wonderful food. In Melbourne, a general practitioner has been doing studies on menopausal women consuming soy flour and wheat flour. She found a 40 per cent reduction in hot flushes in the group of women taking the soy flour compared to a 25 per cent reduction in the group taking wheat flour. Similar well-designed studies with soy extracts worldwide also showed good response to reducing hot flushes in women ingesting soy flour extract. The results have certainly attracted special interest from doctors and their female patients.

Earlier studies have uncovered a marked difference in the hot flushes experienced by Asian and Caucasian women. The low incidence of hot flushes and hip fractures in Asian women was attributed to their diet.

From my own observation, Asian women have been undergoing major changes in their diets over the past twenty to thirty years. Although the genes essentially remain the same, increased affluence has meant increased consumption of highly processed foods and animal products accompanied by a dramatic reduction in the consumption of natural foods and vegetable products. This has contributed to a generation of new women requiring HRT for their unbearable hot flushes. It will be interesting to do a study to confirm this observation.

Soy Drinks: a comparison per 100 mL (3$^1/_2$ fl oz)

Brand	Manufacturer	Energy	Protein	Fat	Carbohydrate	Sugars	Calcium	Sodium	Potassium
			(g)	(g)	(g)	(g)	(g)	(mg)	(mg)	(mg)
Aussie Trim Soy	Pureharvest	220	2.2	1.5	7.3	3.0	130	60	70
Aussie Soy	Pureharvest	269	2.2	2.9	7.3	3.0	NS	60	70
Good Life	Berrivale Orchards	269	3.4	3.4	5.0	2.0	125	65	150
Good Life Low Fat	Berrivale Orchards	176	3.4	0.9	5.0	2.0	125	65	150
So Good	Sanitarium	260	3.4	3.4	4.7	1.6	110	40	140
So Good Lite	Sanitarium	180	3.6	0.5	6.0	2.0	110	40	140
So Natural	Australian Natural Foods (ANF)	266	2.0	2.9	7.4	2.1	NS	90	90
So Natural Lite	ANF	191	2.0	0.9	7.4	2.1	NS	90	90
Soy Drink	Farmland	300	2.8	<1	15.9	2.0	16	30	90
Soy Drink	Home Brand	280	3.4	3.7	5.2	1.8	125	85	150
Soy Drink	No Frills	260	3.4	3.4	4.7	1.6	120	58	140
Soy Extra Lite	Chemist's Own	175	3.4	0.9	5.2	1.8	123	90	210
Soy Extra Premium	Chemist's Own	250	3.4	2.9	5.2	1.8	125	90	210
Soy Drink	Sungold	271	3.7	3.5	4.9	1.9	120	52	126
Vita Soy	Vita Soy International	267	3.6	3.0	5.6	3.6	NS	76	124
Vital Life	ANF	258	1.9	2.8	7.4	2.6	125	90	113.4

NS: not stated

SOYBEAN PASTE

The Asians use soybean paste in their cooking, usually in stews and meat with vegetables dishes. The Japanese also use soybean paste — they call it *miso.*

Not all Asian food stores stock miso paste, but you can find a variety of miso in most Japanese grocery stores. This is a required ingredient for miso soup. There are three main categories of miso — barley miso, rice miso and soybean miso. Do not be misled by the names, all of these pastes contain soybeans, it is merely the base of the mould or *koji* that is used to make the miso that gives it its different names.

The plain, lighter colour miso contains sea salt, fermented soybeans, rice and sometimes barley. The darker varieties may contain all of the above, as well as extracts of bonito (fish), seaweed, sake and amino acids. Abundant Earth distributes five different types of miso or soybean paste: Genii, Hatcho, Mugi, White and Kome Miso in plastic packs weighing 400 grams.

White Miso has more rice content than Kome Miso; Mugi Miso has barley, but no rice; and Hatcho has no rice or barley at all. Genmai Miso has brown rice. All these misos contain an enzyme called *Aspergilus oryzae* (koji), but no extracts of seaweed, sake or bonito.

Use about a level tablespoon to a bowl of water for making soup. Increase the amount according to the water content of your soup. Miso can be used to marinate meats for barbecues and stir-fries, as well as in sauces for vegetables. It will keep for up to a year if stored in an airtight container in the refrigerator.

The Chinese and Southeast Asians sell bean paste in jars. The fermented soybeans are very salty and need to be used sparingly.

SOY FLOUR

This is made from the dehulled or dehusked soybean, which is then milled after a desolventizing, toasting and cooling process. The desolventization process removes the solvent which was added initially to remove the oil.

Soy flour is heavier than wheat flour and is creamy in colour with a distinctive 'beany' smell, but it has a high protein content. The beany smell usually transforms into a rather nutty flavour after cooking. Cakes, biscuits or cookies can be made from soybean flour, but usually in combination with a lighter flour, as soybean flour has a tendency to absorb a lot of moisture during the cooking process.

Soy flour is good for coeliac disease sufferers as it does not contain gluten.

TOFU OR SOYBEAN CURD

Tofu is made from soybean milk. A coagulant is added to the boiling concentrated milk. The Chinese and Vietnamese use calcium sulphate or, in some cases, gypsum. The Japanese tend to use glucono delta lactone, while some manufacturers in Australia use *nigari* to set the curd.

There are different forms of tofu in the supermarkets: silken tofu, firm tofu and hard tofu can be found in the refrigerated section. The UHT or long-life form can be found in amongst the shelves containing other Asian ingredients. Needless to say, the pack has to be refrigerated after opening and consumed within two days of opening.

The Asian supermarkets and food stores stock all of the above, as well as fresh tofu immersed in water in plastic containers in order to keep it fresh.

Silken tofu is best for soups, desserts, sauces and some delicate dishes requiring a smooth texture.

Firm tofu handles cutting quite well and can be added to vegetable dishes or stews.

Hard tofu can be deep-fried for stuffing and barbecuing.

Tofu cutlets are very hard tofu marinated in soy sauce and deep-fried. Hence it is brown in colour on the outside, tastes savoury, but looks white on the inside. You can cut it up for salads, barbecues and stews. It can also be used as a meat substitute and can stand a lot of handling, unlike silken tofu which is very friable.

Deep-fried tofu puffs or *tofu buk* are 2–3 cm ($3/_4$–$1^1/_4$ in) cubes of tofu and light brown in colour. These are very light and airy inside. They can be eaten straight from the packet with a sauce such as dark soy sauce and chillies, or can be used for cooking in certain soups, stuffing with meat or stews. They can be cut up into smaller sizes to add to salads where the sauces will be soaked up by the tofu buk. I suppose it is rather similar to the croutons in a Caesar salad in function.

Tofu desserts come in tubs of 200 g (7 oz) sizes and in a variety of flavours, too. If you cannot find them in the supermarket, I am sure you can pick some up from a health food stores. The Asian food stores stock some tofu desserts in their cold storage sections, in rectangular plastic packs of 300 g (10 oz) size. They look like silken tofu and come in various flavours.

FERMENTED SOYBEAN CURD CUBES

Fermented soybean curd cubes in red or yellow are also used throughout Asia for flavouring meat dishes. These are sold in jars and are readily available in Asian supermarkets or food stores. Dishes made with fermented soybean curd have a very distinct smell and taste. The yellow variety may come in plain, chilli and/or sesame flavour. These can be eaten with plain rice broth or porridge (congee).

DRIED SOYBEAN CURD

Dried soybean curd, also known as *fu pei* or *fu juk*, is the skin that forms on the top of boiling soy milk concentrate. This skin is dried and sold in sheets or in a rolled-up form called 'sticks'. They are either sweet or savoury.

The sweet version is soaked in water for a short time before it is added to the saucepan for cooking as a dessert. Soybean drink can be reconstituted by boiling the sweet soybean curd sheets in water for an hour or so, and sugar added to sweeten the resulting drink.

The savoury rolls or sticks are generally soaked for a longer period of time before cut-up pieces are used for stews. The flat savoury sheets are used to wrap up meats and vegetables before steaming, stewing or deep-frying. This is similar in principle to cabbage rolls, but differs in texture and taste.

Soy Sauce

Soy sauce is made from salted roasted soybeans which have been fermented for a few months to a year in huge vats. It is said that the sauce tastes better if the container is made of wood.

You can get such a variety of soy sauces from the supermarket these days. Basically, there is light soy sauce and dark soy sauce. Most of us use the light variety for marinating meat, fish and poultry, and for making sauces. The dark soy sauce is for special stews and sometimes for sauces as well. Generally speaking, dark soy sauce is sweeter and less salty, and gives meat a lustrous, dark brown colour. The manufacturer may add black beans to the processing; this is known as blackbean soy sauce. Mushrooms are sometimes added to the soy sauce extracts during processing; this is called mushroom soy sauce.

Use soy sauce sparingly if you suffer from kidney disorders and/or high blood pressure (hypertension) because of its high sodium content. If you really must use it, look out for the low-salt (sodium) ones. Kikkoman markets one of the low-salt soy sauces in Australia.

Soybean Shoots

This product must not be confused with mung bean shoots, which are readily available in most supermarkets and local greengrocers. Soybean shoots take longer to cook than mung bean shoots; the roots are slightly stringy and the cotyledons are very bright yellow in colour and thick and broad in structure. This part of the shoot contains the most nutrients and gives it a very nutty taste. You can buy soybean shoots in packets from Asian food stores.

The phytoestrogen (coumestrol) content in the soybean shoot is at least 14 times greater than that found in alfalfa sprouts and 70 times the amount in frozen green or string beans weight for weight. Like the mung bean shoot, the soybean shoot is also a good source of vitamin C.

Both beans can be sprouted at home for your convenience. Mung bean shoots are much easier to get, while soybean shoots can sometimes be hard to find as they do not keep as well as mung bean shoots.

Use very fresh beans for sprouting. Pre-soak the soybeans in cold water overnight. Sow onto a supporting porous bed in a clean container and keep in an airy place away from sunlight. Water twice daily and drain the water so that the sprouting beans are not soaking in water at all times. The bean sprouts will be ready to harvest in 4 days. Remove the skin before cooking. The sprouts can be kept for 2 days in the refrigerator after harvesting.

LECITHIN

Lecithin is made from soybeans and is an anti-oxidant good for the control of cholesterol. It is available in powdered form, tablet form and in combination with other vitamins and minerals. It can also be bought in a granulated form imported from the United States but packaged in Australia. You can add the powder or granules to milk shakes, eggnogs, soups and salads, or sprinkle them over your breakfast cereal.

SOYBEAN OIL

Soybean oil is an extract from soybeans. The edible refined oil is good for deep-frying your foods as it contains no cholesterol and produces very little smoke at high cooking temperatures. Other advantages are the fact that it contains high levels of omega-3 and omega-6 fatty acids, as well as linolenic acid and linoleic acid (vitamin F) which is said to help in the prevention of bowel and breast cancers.

You can use soybean oil for stir-frying vegetables, or add it to cake, biscuit or cookie batters. It is available from Asian food stores in 1-litre (1-quart) or 2-litre (2-quart) plastic containers. Some supermarkets stock 750 mL (1½ pint) containers and the price is similar to canola oil.

Many products are made from soybean oil, but it is beyond the scope of this book to discuss them all.

TEMPEH

Tempeh is another soy product marketed in vacuum-sealed plastic bags. It is made from fermented whole soybeans compressed into blocks for easy handling. It can be sliced and marinated prior to frying, grilling (broiling) or barbecuing. It is a rich source of proteins, vitamin B (especially B12), iron, potassium and calcium.

It is generally found in the cold storage section of health food stores and comes in various flavours. It is high in fibre and rich in phytoestrogens.

OTHER SOY PRODUCTS

Soy cheeses are now available and are rather tasty. You should be able to find them in the refrigerated section of the supermarket next to the tofu. They come in a good selection of flavours from mild to chilli hot! Use as a substitute for cheese in quiches, samosas, pizzas, lasagne and the like.

Tofu ice cream or frozen desserts are available, but usually hard to find in the supermarkets in Australia. This is probably due to the low demand for this product. When demand increases these products will probably be more readily available.

In the United States, *tofu salad dressing* is available and is similar to mayonnaise. Only recently, *tofu mayonnaise* has appeared in jars on the shelves of some supermarkets and health food stores. Those of you who like to make your own can find a recipe for Tofu Mayonnaise on page 49.

You can also find *soya mayonnaise* in jars on the supermarket shelves. This product contains whole eggs and therefore is not cholesterol-free. *Tofu burgers* in vacuum-sealed bags and *chicken burgers* containing soybeans and chickpeas (garbanzo beans) are available for those of us who are tired of beef burgers or hamburgers. They only require heating before being inserted in a hamburger roll.

Soy cookies by Naytura have a high fibre content. It certainly beats baking your own soy cookies when you have a million other things to do.

Ryvita country grains crispbread contains soy kibble as well as other phytoestrogen-rich seeds and grains. This makes a great snack or alternative to breads for cut lunches. *Ryvita Soy-Lin* crispbread is a new product containing rice flour, soy, rye meal, linola and linseed.

Savoury snacks such as *soy chips* and *soy sticks* are very delicious. A Sydney company manufactures some of these products marketed under the brand name 'Soya King'. Another Melbourne company imports soy snacks from Indonesia and packages them in Australia before marketing them.

Lasagne pasta made from soy and rice flour is available in health food stores. *Soyaroni* is a local pasta containing soy which now graces the supermarket shelves. This is a very tasty pasta which cooks in 12 minutes.

Soy bread is being marketed in Australia in response to research findings into the benefits of soy and linseed in menopausal women. This bread is delicious — soft in texture and nutty in flavour. You can find it listed as *Burgen Soy and Linseed loaf* and it is marketed by Tip Top Bakeries. Vogel has produced a similar soy and linseed bread, too. Watch out for that if you cannot find your favourite soy bread.

Recently, Buttercup has started producing a low-fat soy and linseed bread called Molenberg Soy and Linseed. This has 2.4 g of fat per 2 slices compared with 7.1 g in the Burgen Soy and Linseed loaf.

Country Life Bakery in Victoria has been marketing *Hi Soy* bread since late 1996, following the release of research on the benefits of soy flour.

Soy chunks and *soy grits* are also available from speciality stores. They are marketed in plastic bags by Soy Products of Australia Pty Ltd, which is based in Melbourne. Most health food stores carry their products. Soy chunks are a pre-cooked powder containing soy, rice, wholegrain maize and other healthy grains and seeds. It requires mixing with your favourite drink or hot water before consuming.

Soy grits are high in protein and require pre-soaking before they can be used in cooking. The skin has been removed from the soybean prior to light steaming of the crushed product. You can use soy grits to make soybean milk by soaking them overnight in hot water. The grits are then blended as described in the recipe for making soybean drink on page 50. The resulting milk is not as rich as the one made from raw soybeans. Soy grits can also be added to muesli, bread, meat loaves, soups and casseroles.

Soy yoghurt is available from the cold storage section of most supermarkets. This comes in 200 g (7 oz) tubs in six lovely flavours — vanilla, fruit salad, peach and mango, passionfruit, wildberry and strawberry.

Soya polyunsaturated margarine is marketed by Naytura and can also be found in the cold storage section of some supermarkets.

More recently, a very delicious *soy smoothie* with a low-fat soy milk base can be found in the refrigerated sections of supermarkets. The rich flavours of banana, and mango smoothies come in 1 litre (1 quart) or 500 mL (16 fl oz) cartons. You can also find soy smoothies in smaller UHT or long-life packs.

CHAPTER FOUR

SOY MEALS
AND SOY UNITS

As soy contains the most powerful of the isoflavones, and has been used extensively in research into the biological effects in humans and animals, food scientists often refer to a specified quantity of soy products as a 'soy meal' as a frame of reference. In this book I refer to it as one soy unit.

A soy meal or unit is equivalent to 1 cup (250 mL, 8 fl oz) of soy milk. However, as some soy milks are much lower in soy protein than others, the quantity may sometimes be extended to $1^1/_4$ cups (300 mL, 10 fl oz) for the milk with the lower soy protein content. The isoflavone content in soy products is proportional to the soy protein content.

Research into the effects of phytoestrogens and cardiovascular disease found that the maximum beneficial effect of soy on blood pressure requires an intake of 2 soy units per day. It has been recommended that these be taken in two divided doses, i.e. one soy unit in the morning and one at night.

While it is quite simple for scientists to say 'eat 1 soy unit' or 'eat 2 soy units', at present most readers would only recognise what quantity this means in terms of soy milk. What about soy units in relation to other soy products? This is the crucial question in the minds of people seeking information and help regarding the natural estrogen diet.

Soy Unit Equivalents
One soy unit is equivalent to:

1 cup (250 mL, 8 fl oz) of soy milk

20 g	soy milk powder	65 g	soyaroni pasta
25 g	dried soybeans	75 g	miso (mixture)
25 g	soy flour	80 g	cooked soybeans
25 g	soy grits	100 g	tofu cubes (puffs)
40 g	tempeh	110 g	silken tofu
45 g	tofu cutlet	135 g	sprouted soybeans
50 g	miso (pure) or soybean paste	200 g	soy yoghurt
55 g	soy cheese	200 g	soybean curd sheets

Soy Unit Content in the Recipes in This Book

The soy unit content in the selected recipes is calculated to the nearest 0.25 (one-quarter) of a soy unit. The figures given are for the whole recipe. The soy unit content of a serving will depend on the number of portions into which you have eventually divided the recipe. Some people are small eaters, while others need to eat more to feel satisfied.

Recipe	Soy Unit Content
Apple and Potato Salad	0.75
Apple Muffins	3.75
Baked Stuffed Pumpkin	1.75* (soy cheese)
Baked Soybeans in Eggplant	1.5
Banana Soy Drink	0.75
Bean Curd and Barley Dessert	0.5
Bean Salad	2.5
Cherry Muffins	3.75
Chicken and Potato Curry	1.5
Creamy Corn Soup	1.5
Creamy Pumpkin Soup	1.5
Curried Tofu and Vegetables	2.5
Fried Rice Vermicelli	2.25
Gado Gado	5.25
Marrow and Tofu Soup	2.75
Miso Soup	1.5
Potato Casserole in Tofu Sauce	2.5
Rockmelon Soy Milkshake	2.25
Shredded Beef with Bean Curd	2.5
Soy Agar-Agar	2.0
Soy and Oatmeal Cookies	1.0 in 12 cookies
Soy Apple Cake	2.25
Soybean Dip	2.0
Soybean Drink	1.0 in 1 1/4 cups (300 mL, 10 fl oz)
Soybeans in Tomato Sauce	4.0
Soybean Marrow Soup	4.0
Soybean Shoots and Prawns	1.5

Soybean Shoots with Minced Pork	3.0
Soybean Shoots with Shredded Beef	1.5
Soybean Vindaloo	5.0
Soy Carrot Cake	1.75
Soy Curd Dessert	3.75
Soy Curry Puffs	2.25
Soy Jaffles	1.5
Soy Pancakes (Pikelets)	2.5
Soyaroni Salad	4.0
Soyaroni Salmon Casserole	
without soy cheese	6.0
with soy cheese	9.5
Steam Boat	5.5
Steamed Fish Fillet with Tofu	2.75
Steamed Tofu and Egg	1.5
Stewed Beancurd Sticks and Wood Fungus	0.5
Sticky Rice Pudding	2.0
Stir-fried Snow Peas and Tofu	2.75
Stir-fried Tempeh and Vegetables	2.5
Stir-fried Tofu Cutlet with Vegetables	2.25
Strawberry Soy Drink	0.75
Strawberry Soy Dessert	0.75
Stuffed Tofu and Soy Cheese Sauce	6.0
Stuffed Tofu Cubes	2.5
Sweet and Sour Tempeh	3.5
Sweet and Sour Tofu	2.75
Thai Salad	1.25
Tofu Cutlets in Lettuce Leaves	2.25
Tofu in Oyster Sauce	2.75
Tofu Mayonnaise	0.75 in 100 mL ($3^1/_2$ fl oz)
Tofu with Minced Meat	2.75
Wheat Noodles with Tofu Cutlet	2.25

PART II

✣

RECIPES

CONVERSION TABLES

g : grams	**mL** : millilitre	**mm** : millimetre
kg : kilogram	**L** : litre	**cm** : centimetre

1 teaspoon :		5 mL	
1 tablespoon :	**4 teaspoons :**	20 mL (Australia)	
1 tablespoon :	**3 teaspoons :**	15 mL (USA and UK)	
1 cup :		250 mL :	8 fl oz

1 g :	0.035 ounce
30 g :	1 ounce

1 cm :	0.4 inch
2.5 cm :	1 inch

30 mL :		1 fl oz	
625 mL :	**2$^1/_2$ cups :**	20 fl oz :	1 imp. pint

OVEN TEMPERATURES AND GAS MARKS

CELCIUS	FAHRENHEIT	GAS MARK	HEAT
110°C	225°F	$^1/_4$ (S)	very cool
120°C	250°F	$^1/_2$ (S)	very cool
140°C	275°F	1	cool
150°C	300°F	2	cool
160°C	325°F	3	moderate
180°C	350°F	4	moderate
190°C	375°F	5	fairly hot
200°C	400°F	6	fairly hot
220°C	425°F	7	hot
230°C	450°F	8	very hot
240°C	475°F	9	very hot
260°C	500°F	10	very very hot

Note: The gas mark 'S' is a special setting available on some ovens and is used for cooking slowly, e.g. meringues.

INTRODUCTORY NOTES

The energy, cholesterol and calcium content of all the recipes (except the Steam Boat) were calculated by Ms Jenny Chan, who is a practising consultant dietitian and nutritionist in Liverpool, New South Wales. She is also a part-time lecturer at the University of Sydney and currently researching her Ph.D. thesis. I am deeply grateful for her assistance.

The total energy, cholesterol and calcium content is listed for each recipe except the Steam Boat (see page 94 for explanation). As serving size varies between households and between individuals depending on appetite, the net value of energy, cholesterol and calcium can be obtained by dividing the total value by the number of servings obtained from that particular dish.

If you are on a low-cholesterol diet, try to keep your daily cholesterol intake less than 200 milligrams per day. Substitute high-cholesterol foods such as eggs with scramblers and also avoid prawns (shrimp).

Those people watching their weight can use low-fat soy milk and defatted soy flour, although the latter can be difficult to find. Hopefully defatted soy flour will become a common item in the supermarkets and food stores in the future.

For those of you cooking for several people in a household, you can add chicken or meat to the recipes so that the rest of the family is not missing out on their preferred protein. For example, in stir-fry dishes with tempeh or tofu cutlet, add some diced chicken for those who may not like these two ingredients.

The following abbreviations are used:

Cal : kilocalorie   kJ : kilojoule   Chol : cholesterol   Ca : Calcium

CHICKPEA DIP (HUMMUS)

Cal : 612   kJ : 2534   Chol : 0 mg   Ca : 303 mg

1 cup (200 g, 7 oz) cooked chickpeas (garbanzo beans)
3 cloves garlic, peeled
3 tablespoons tahini
3 tablespoons boiling water
1 level teaspoon salt
$^1/_4$ teaspoon ground black pepper
2 tablespoons lemon juice

Place all the ingredients in a blender or food processor, and blend until smooth. Add more lemon juice if desired.

Serve with raw vegetables or savoury biscuits as a dip, or serve on top of baked potatoes.

Note: If using dried chickpeas, rinse with cold water and discard any bad chickpeas. Soak in plenty of cold water overnight. Drain and rinse chickpeas again, then bring to the boil with water in a large saucepan. Simmer for 30 minutes. Add $^1/_2$ teaspoon salt halfway through the simmering time. About 100 g ($3^1/_2$ oz) of dried chickpeas cook to 200–210 g (7 oz) in final weight.

Tahini is available from health food stores and most supermarkets. It is made from ground or milled sesame seeds and is very rich in proteins, calcium, phosphorus and vitamin E. Tahini also contains phytoestrogens.
Chickpeas are quite sweet by themselves and have a very nice flavour. Most people can eat them unflavoured. Roasted chickpeas are commonly eaten as a savoury snack by young and old in Southeast Asian countries.

SOYBEAN DIP

Cal : 440   kJ : 1824   Chol : 26 mg   Ca : 140 mg

2 teaspoons (10–15 g, $^1/_2$ oz) red or Italian onion, finely chopped
1 tablespoon soybean oil
1 teaspoon curry powder
3 teaspoons water
$^3/_4$ cup (150 g, 5 oz) cooked soybeans
$^3/_4$ teaspoon salt
1 tablespoon boiling water
1 tablespoon sour cream or natural (plain) yoghurt

Place the onion and soybean oil in a small frying pan or skillet over a medium heat. Mix the curry powder and water into a paste and add to the pan. Sauté for a few minutes, until fragrant but not dry.

Blend or process the curry mixture, soybeans, salt, boiling water and sour cream until smooth.

Serve with raw vegetables, water crackers or other savoury crackers as desired. This dip can be spread on bread and lightly toasted under the griller (broiler).

Dried soybeans can be obtained from most supermarkets, health food stores and Asian grocery stores. They take a long time to cook compared to other pulses, but soaking for 24 hours or at least overnight prior to cooking will decrease the cooking time. See page 65 for instructions on how to cook soybeans.
The cooked soybeans can be frozen in suitable-sized containers for easy defrosting of the beans for use in the various recipes found in this cookbook. Rinse the defrosted cooked beans in hot water before using in this recipe.

SPICY LENTIL DIP

Cal : 731   kJ : 3040   Chol : 0 mg   Ca : 157 mg

1 cup (200 g, 7 oz) lentils, rinsed and picked over
1/2 small onion, finely chopped
1 tablespoon soybean oil
1 red chilli pepper, seeded and finely chopped
1 heaped teaspoon finely chopped fresh ginger
1/2 teaspoon ground cumin
1/4 teaspoon ground turmeric
1 1/2 cups (625 mL, 10 fl oz) water
1/2 stock cube
1/2 teaspoon garam masala
1/2 teaspoon salt
2 tablespoons coconut powder

Soak the lentils in cold water.

Place the onion and soybean oil in a saucepan over a medium heat. Sauté until the onion is translucent and starting to brown. Add the chilli and ginger, and continue to sauté, stirring, for 2 minutes. Add the cumin and turmeric and stir through well.

Drain the lentils and add to the mixture in the saucepan. Stir for 3–4 minutes before adding the water. Reduce the heat to very low and simmer for 15 minutes.

Add the stock cube, garam masala, salt and coconut powder. Cook for a further 10–15 minutes. Allow to cool before putting in the food processor and blending for 2 minutes.

Serve cold with raw vegetables or savoury crackers. This dip can also be served hot with steamed rice.

Lentils are rich in fibre, proteins, iron and potassium. This legume also contains phytoestrogens.

TOFU MAYONNAISE

Cal : 299   kJ : 1256   Chol : 0 mg   Ca : 107 mg

150 g (5 oz) tofu, preferably silken tofu
1 tablespoon boiling water
2 stalks fresh chives
$2^1/_2$ teaspoons white vinegar
1 tablespoon olive oil
2 teaspoons sugar
$^1/_2$ teaspoon salt
$^1/_2$ teaspoon English or other hot mustard

Place all the ingredients in a blender or food processor. Blend for 30 seconds. Scrape down the sides of the blender and blend again until a smooth consistency is achieved.

Transfer the mayonnaise to a clean airtight container and store in the refrigerator until ready to use.

MAKES ABOUT $^3/_4$ CUP (185 ML, 6 FL OZ)

Lemon or lime juice can be used in place of the vinegar, but vinegar has some preservative properties. Hence, your mayonnaise can keep for a few days longer if made with vinegar rather than lemon or lime juice.
Silken tofu is best for this recipe and it must be fresh. The vacuum-sealed packs are more likely to be superior.

SOYBEAN DRINK

Cal : 985   kJ : 4072   Chol : 0 mg   Ca : 361mg

scant 1 cup (200 g, 7 oz) dried soybeans, rinsed and picked over
1.5 litres (1$^1/_2$ quarts, 2$^1/_2$ imp. pints) water
4–5 tablespoons sugar

Soak the soybeans in cold water for 12–24 hours.

Drain and rub the beans between your hands to loosen the skins. Discard as much skin as possible.

Place half the beans in a blender or food processor with about $^3/_4$–1$^1/_4$ cups (185–310 mL, 6–10 fl oz) of the water. Repeat with the remaining beans.

Using fine cheesecloth or muslin bag, strain all the liquid from the beans into a large boiler or saucepan by squeezing the bag.

Blend the bean residue *(okara)* again, adding more of the water and strain once again into the boiler. You can repeat this twice in order to get the maximum milk out of the beans. Discard the bean residue and then strain the contents of the boiler one more time.

Bring the soybean milk to the boil and simmer for 2–3 minutes.

Add the sugar according to taste and store the milk in the refrigerator until ready to use.

Soybean milk made this way keeps longer if the sugar is not added before the milk is stored in the refrigerator.
Simply add sugar, artificial sweetener or glucose as desired when you are ready to use.
If you want a concentrated drink, add less water during processing.
This recipe is unsuitable for infant feeding as it is not fortifed with all the essential ingredients required for a baby's growth.

BANANA-FLAVOURED
SOY DRINK

Cal : 283   kJ : 1153   Chol : 0 mg   Ca : 226 mg

1 ripe banana, cut into small pieces
1–2 teaspoons sugar or artificial sweetener
scant 1 cup (225 mL, 7 fl oz) soy milk
3–4 drops vanilla essence (extract) (optional)

Pour the soy milk into a blender or food processor. Add the banana and sugar to taste, and the vanilla essence if using. Blend for 30 seconds. Chill before serving.

Avoid bananas if you are suffering from reflux problems as this usually aggravates the condition. Also, use bananas sparingly if you suffer from joint pain.

ROCKMELON
SOY MILK SHAKE

Cal : 356   kJ : 1495   Chol : 0 mg   Ca : 258 mg

250 g (8 oz) rockmelon (cantaloupe), peeled and diced
1 tablespoon rich dark honey
scant $1/2$ cup (100 mL, $3^1/2$ fl oz) fresh soy milk
200 g (7 oz) silken tofu

Place all the ingredients into a blender or food processor. Blend for 1 minute. Chill before serving.
MAKES ABOUT $3^1/4$ CUPS (800 ML, 26 FL OZ)

Rockmelons are rich in beta carotene, a compound linked to a lower lung cancer rate. Rockmelons also have blood-thinning properties as they inhibit platelet aggregation, thus reducing the risk of blood clots forming within the blood vessels.

STRAWBERRY SOY DRINK

Cal : 154   kJ : 633   Chol : 0 mg   Ca : 38 mg

scant 1 cup (200 mL, 7 fl oz) soy milk
2–3 teaspoons sugar or artificial sweetener
100 g (3$^1/_2$ oz) strawberries, washed, hulled and sliced

Pour the soy milk into a blender or food processor. Add the sugar to taste and the strawberries. Blend for 30 seconds. Chill before serving.

Commercially prepared soy milk is readily available. The UHT or long-life soy milk tastes different from homemade soy milk. Some preparations are fat reduced and this is particularly good for those on a weight reduction diet. Some brands are calcium enriched and therefore good for those who need more dietary calcium.
Some brands of soy milk are already flavoured and come in 250 mL (8 fl oz) UHT packages, making them convenient for lunch or picnic packs.

SOY JAFFLES

Cal : 383   kJ : 1610   Chol : < 1 mg using margarine   Ca : 223 mg

2 slices soy and linseed bread
1 teaspoon butter or margarine
1 handful alfalfa sprouts, plus extra for garnish
1 tablespoon shredded carrot
30 g (1 oz) soy cheese, grated
salt and freshly ground black pepper, to taste
cherry tomatoes, for garnish (optional)

Warm a jaffle maker.

Spread the bread thinly with the butter. Grease one section of the jaffle maker with the remaining butter.

Place one slice of bread buttered side down in the jaffle maker. Pile on the alfalfa sprouts, carrots and soy cheese. Season with salt and pepper to taste.

Cover with the second slice of soy bread, this time buttered side up. Close the lid of the jaffle maker and cook for 3–4 minutes.

Slice the sandwich in half diagonally using kitchen scissors or a sharp knife. Serve garnished with the extra alfalfa sprouts and cherry tomatoes (if using).

Note: If you do not own a jaffle maker, toast the bread lightly on one side under a hot grill (broiler), then place the open sandwiches back under the grill until the soy cheese has melted.

Alfalfa sprouts are a rich source of lignans, coumestans and vitamin C. As they are very light in weight, a packet of fresh sprouts will last a few meals. Some people will object to its green, beany taste, but this almost disappears when cooked inside the jaffle. Those who do not object to the taste can eat alfalfa sprouts raw as an accompaniment to other salads or as a garnish to the recipe above.

CHICKEN STOCK

Cal : 160   kJ : 671   Chol : < 1 mg   Ca : 4 mg

625 g (1 1/4 lb) chicken bones
2 litres (2 quarts, 3 1/4 imp. pints) water
2 slices fresh ginger
5 white peppercorns

Remove all visible fat on the chicken bones before placing them in a pressure cooker with the water.

Add the ginger and peppercorns. Cook until pressurised, then lower the heat to continue cooking for another 30 minutes.

Allow the stock to cool, then skim any fat off the top and discard.

Store in the refrigerator or freezer until ready to use. If you are freezing the stock for use at a later date, it may be more convenient to divide it into portions suitable for use in recipes. This way you only defrost the amount you need each time a recipe calls for stock. Frozen stock keeps for 4 weeks. Refrigerated stock keeps 3–4 days only.

Note: If you are not using a pressure cooker, place the ingredients in a large boiler or saucepan and add an extra 2 cups (500 mL, 16 fl oz) water. Bring to the boil and simmer for at least 2 hours before using.

Stock made from bones tends to give higher calcium content. This can be facilitated by adding 1 tablespoon apple cider vinegar to the cooking pot.
When beef stock is required, use 1 kg (2 lb) beef bones instead of chicken bones. Pork bones can also be used to make stock using the above method.
Any fat that you have not skimmed off will be very easy to remove once the stock has been chilled or frozen.

CHICKEN AND DONG QUAI SOUP

Cal : 257   kJ : 1086   Chol : 100 mg   Ca : 19 mg

7 red dates, about 10 g ($^1/_2$ oz)
5–6 g ($^1/_4$ oz) dong quai root or slices, washed
2$^1/_2$ cups (625 mL, 24 fl oz) water
200 g (7 oz) chicken breast fillet, cut into 2–3 cm ($^3/_4$–1$^1/_4$ in) chunks
pinch or two of salt

Soak the red dates in warm water, replacing any bad ones.

Place the dong quai in a small saucepan. Add the water and chicken. Gently bruise the red dates with the side of a chopper in order to efficiently release the flavour, then add these to the saucepan as well.

Bring to the boil and simmer over a very low heat for 2–2$^1/_2$ hours, checking that the soup does not evaporate too quickly. Add more water if necessary. About 1 cup (250 mL, 8 fl oz) of soup should be left in the saucepan at the end of cooking.

Add salt to taste and drink warm before retiring to bed.

SERVES ONE

Note: Take once a month only. If still menstruating, wait until a few days after your period has finished before drinking. It is important to keep to the weight specified above, as this is a potent Chinese herb. The whole root and pre-sliced segments vary greatly in size and weight. Too much of this herb causes headaches, pimples, skin eruptions, sore throats and constipation.

Dong quai or tang kwei is Angelica sinensis and possesses a strong aroma with a slightly bitter aftertaste. Some varieties are not bitter, but considered 'sweet'.

In traditional Chinese medicine, dong quai is used by men as well as women to stimulate appetite, strengthen the body and improve the immune system. It contains phytoestrogens and is used in combination with other herbs for treatment of menstrual disorders and menopausal symptoms.

Health food stores sell dong quai in capsule form or tincture.

MISO SOUP

Cal : 112 mg   kJ : 470   Chol : 0 mg   Ca : 93 mg

1 cup (250 mL, 8 fl oz) water
dashi stock paste (or concentrate if using plain miso paste)
1 spring (green) onion, green part only, cut into 2 cm ($^3/_4$ in) lengths
100 g ($3^1/_2$ oz) tofu, cut into 1–2 cm ($^1/_2$–$^3/_4$ in) cubes
1 level tablespoon miso paste

Bring the water to the boil in a small saucepan. Add the dashi stock
(if using) and allow to boil for 2–3 minutes. Add the spring onion and tofu.
    Add a small amount of water to the miso paste to dissolve evenly
before adding to soup. Bring to boil and serve in a deep bowl.
SERVES ONE

Note: Firm tofu is normally used, but some people may like to use silken
tofu instead as it is very smooth and friable.

Miso soup is a popular Japanese breakfast dish
for women and men.
There are five types of miso paste, as well as ones with the
dashi concentrate incorporated into the miso. Please read the
contents of the package carefully before making your purchase.
The marukome miso has the dashi concentrate added. Hence
there is no need to add dashi stock paste or concentrate to the
recipe if using this brand.

CREAMY CORN SOUP

Cal : 726   kJ : 3049   Chol : 294 mg   Ca : 143 mg

2 tablespoons cornflour (cornstarch)
1 tablespoon light soy sauce
50 g (2 oz) chicken breast fillet, cut into thin strips
4 cups (1 litre, 1$^3/_4$ imp. pints) chicken stock
1 can (420 g, 13 oz) creamed corn
150 g (5 oz) silken tofu
$^1/_4$ cup (60 mL, 2 fl oz) water
1 large egg, beaten
salt, to taste

Blend $^1/_2$ tablespoon of the cornflour with the soy sauce. Add the chicken strips and allow to marinate.

Bring the chicken stock to the boil in a large saucepan. When boiling, add the marinated chicken. Cook for 5 minutes before adding the creamed corn.

Blend or process the tofu and water for 1 minute. Add blended tofu and the egg to the soup mixture, stirring all the time.

Mix the remaining cornflour into a paste using a little water, then use to thicken the soup. Add salt according to taste or dietary restrictions. Serve hot.

SERVES 4–6

Use the homemade chicken stock given on page 54. If you are using a canned stock, add water to make up to 4 cups
(1 litre, 1$^3/_4$ imp. pints).
This is a very creamy and tasty recipe. Omit the tofu if you do not want a creamy taste.
Add extra cornflour if a thicker soup is desired.
Both the corn and tofu in this recipe contain phytoestrogens.
Omit the egg if you are on a low-cholesterol diet.

CREAMY PUMPKIN SOUP

Cal : 624   kJ : 2554   Chol : 0 mg   Ca : 614 mg

500 g (1 lb) pumpkin, diced
100 g (5 oz) apple, peeled and diced
100 g (5 oz) potatoes, peeled and diced
100 g (5 oz) onions, peeled and diced
1²/₃ cups (400 mL, 13 fl oz) water, plus 2 teaspoons extra
1 chicken stock cube
1 ²/₃ cups (400 mL, 13 fl oz) soy milk
1 tablespoon cornfour (cornstarch)
salt and freshly ground black pepper, to taste
sprigs of fresh parsley, to garnish

Place the pumpkin, apple, potatoes and onion into a large saucepan. Add the 1²/₃ cups (400 mL, 13 fl oz) water and the stock cube.

Bring to the boil and simmer for 20 minutes.

Blend or process the soup mixture until smooth, then return to the pan. Add the soy milk and bring to the boil once more.

Mix the cornflour with the extra 2 teaspoons water and add to the soup. Allow to thicken slightly before adding salt and pepper to taste. Garnish with parsley (if using) and serve hot.

SERVES 4–6

The pumpkin, apple and potato in this recipe
all contain phytoestrogens.
Use homemade chicken stock if available (see page 54).
Alternatively, you can use a can of chicken stock to save time.
If a creamier soup is desired, replace the soy milk with 150 g
(5 oz) silken tofu blended into a smooth purée with 1²/₃ cups
(400 mL, 13 fl oz) water.

ABC SOUP

Cal : 944   kJ : 3964   Chol : 335 mg   Ca : 112 mg

500 g (1 lb) gravy beef, cut into 2 cm (³/₄ in) cubes
9 cups (2.25 litres, 3¹/₂ imp. pints) water
3 ripe tomatoes, about 400 g (13 oz), quartered
1 large onion, peeled and quartered
5 cabbage leaves, roughly chopped
1 packet powdered tomato soup
¹/₂ cup (75 g, 2¹/₂ oz) alphabet pasta
salt and freshly ground black pepper, to taste

Bring the beef and 8 cups (2 litres, 3¹/₄ imp. pints) of water to the boil in a large saucepan or boiler. Allow to simmer for 2 hours.

Add the tomatoes, onion and cabbage to the soup mixture.

Soak the pasta in the remaining 1 cup (250 mL, 8 fl oz) water.

Cook the soup mixture for a further 20 minutes, then add the soaked pasta. Stir well to prevent the pasta from forming clumps.

Add the powdered tomato soup and salt and pepper to taste. Cook for a further 10 minutes before serving hot.

SERVES 4–6

Silken tofu cut into 2 cm (³/₄ in) cubes can be added to individual soup bowls just before serving if desired.
The cabbage and alphabet pasta in this recipe contain phytoestrogens.
Leftover soup can be heated for breakfast — adding some fine rice vermicelli will make it a filling and hearty breakfast item, especially in the colder months.
Please avoid this recipe if you suffer from oesophageal reflux problems.

VEGETABLE SOUP

Cal : 3024   KJ : 12618   Chol : 380 mg   Ca : 422 mg

$^1/_2$ cup (90 g, 3 oz) red lentils, rinsed and picked over
$^1/_4$ cup (50 g, 2 oz) white pearl barley, rinsed and picked over
8 cups (2 litres, 3$^1/_4$ imp. pints) pork or chicken stock
2 large potatoes, about 400 g (13 oz), diced
1 carrot, about 100 g (3$^1/_2$ oz), diced
3 tomatoes, about 400 g (13 oz), diced
1 onion, about 100 g (3$^1/_2$ oz), diced
sprigs of fresh parsley, to garnish (optional)

Bring the lentils, pearl parley and stock to the boil in a large saucepan. Allow to simmer for 1 hour.

Add the potatoes, carrot, tomatoes and onion to the soup mixture. Simmer for a further 40 minutes.

Serve hot, garnished with the parsley (if using).

SERVES 4–6

Note: Instead of using soup stock, you can use 1 kg (2 lb) pork bones or chicken bones, and remove the bones before adding the vegetables.

For those who are unable to eat onions and tomatoes,
use celery instead.
Packet soup mixes containing pearl barley, split peas, lentils and
so on can be used instead of the lentils and pearl barley.
The pearl barley, red lentils, carrots and potatoes in this recipe
all contain phytoestrogens.

SOYBEAN AND MARROW SOUP

Cal : 1606   kJ : 6685   Chol : 315 mg   Ca : 350 mg

$1/2$ cup (125 g, 4 oz) dried soybeans
8 cups (2 litres, $3^1/4$ imp. pints) water
500 g (1 lb) barbecued pork ribs or bacon bones
500 g (1 lb) marrow, skin and seeds removed and
cut into 5 cm (2 in) chunks
salt, to taste

Soak the soybeans overnight in hot water, changing the water at least once and discarding any bad beans or debris.

Rinse the soybeans and place in a large saucepan with the water. Bring to the boil and simmer for 40 minutes. Add the pork ribs and simmer for a further 2 hours.

Now add the marrow to the soup mixture and cook for a further 30 minutes.

Just before serving, add salt to taste. Serve the soup hot with some pieces of marrow and soft soybeans in each serving.
SERVES 4–6

Marrow is a seasonal produce so it may not be available
throughout the year.
Asians consider marrow to be a very cooling vegetable and
used in traditional medicines as an adjuvant in
the treatment of fevers.
Some cooks use cubed firm tofu in this dish instead of soybeans,
but it should be noted that when tofu is boiled for a long time,
it tends to be spongy and airy inside.
Cubed silken tofu can also be used, but should be added only
at the last minute, just before serving.

MARROW AND TOFU SOUP

Cal : 2676   kJ : 11239   Chol : 437 mg   Ca : 693 mg

12 dried shiitake mushrooms
8 cups (2 litres, 3^1/$_4$ imp. pints) chicken stock
12 dried oysters, washed
1 kg (2 lb) winter marrow, skin and seeds removed,
cut into 3 cm (1^1/$_4$ in) cubes
300 g (10 oz) firm tofu, cut into 2 cm (^{3}/$_4$ in) cubes
2 spring (green) onions, green part only, diced

Soak the mushrooms in hot water, about 20 minutes. Rinse them with clean water, removing any debris or woody elements.

Place the whole mushrooms, chicken stock, oysters and marrow in a large saucepan. Bring to the boil and simmer for 1 hour.

Add the tofu to the soup and bring to the boil once again.

Serve the soup hot, with a few mushrooms, oysters, tofu and marrow in each bowl. Sprinkle a little spring onion over the top of each serving as a garnish.

SERVES 4–6

Note: Firm tofu is normally used in this recipe as tofu becomes very spongy after prolonged boiling.

Shiitake mushrooms are sold dried and
can be purchased from Asian food stores.
This is a cooling soup, especially for dry and sore throats.
It contains lentinen, which is good for fighting infections.
The marrow and tofu both contain phytoestrogens.
Dried oysters are low in cholesterol and high in zinc and iron.
These can also be purchased from Asian food stores.

SOYBEANS IN TOMATO SAUCE

Cal : 1802   kJ : 7498   Chol : 2 mg   Ca : 801 mg

2 cups (400 g, 13 oz) dried soybeans
3$^1/_4$ cups (800 mL, 26 fl oz) water
6 medium tomatoes, about 500 g (1 lb)
1 tablespoon soybean oil
1 medium onion, diced
2 bay leaves
1 teaspoon salt
1 tablespoon sugar
1 tablespoon chicken stock
3 tablespoons tomato ketchup
1 tablespoon cornflour (cornstarch)

Soak the soybeans overnight in hot water, changing the water at least once and discarding any bad beans or debris.

Rinse the soybeans and place in a pressure cooker with the water. Cook until pressurised, then continue cooking for another 30 minutes. Drain the beans and reserve the cooking water.

Score the skins of the tomatoes with a sharp knife, then blanch in boiling water. Peel off the skins and discard, then dice the flesh.

Heat the soybean oil in a large, deep saucepan. Add the onion and sauté for a few minutes, or until starting to brown. Add the drained soybeans and diced tomatoes and sauté for a little longer.

Add the bay leaves, salt, chicken stock, sugar, tomato ketchup and the reserved cooking water. Cook over a low heat for 25 minutes.

Remove the bay leaves. Mix the cornflour with 1 tablespoon water and add to the cooking pot. Allow to thicken slightly.

Serve hot or store in airtight container in the refrigerator or freezer until ready to use.

Dried soybeans, when cooked in a pressure cooker, will double in volume. They take about 3 hours to cook if using a saucepan rather than a pressure cooker.

CHICKPEA SALAD

Cal : 511   kJ : 2123   Chol : 0 mg   Ca : 177 mg

1 1/2 cups (280 g, 9 oz) cooked chickpeas (garbanzo beans),
rinsed well and drained
1 cup (250 g, 8 oz) diced tomatoes
1/2 cup (60 g, 2 oz) diced celery
6 stalks fresh chives, finely chopped
2 sweet basil leaves, finely chopped

Dressing
2 cloves garlic, diced
1 tablespoon oil
1/4 teaspoon ground black pepper
1/4 teaspoon ground cinnamon
1/2 teaspoon salt
1 teaspoon sugar
1 tablespoon lemon juice
1 tablespoon light soy sauce

Make the dressing first. Sauté the garlic in the oil until golden brown.
Discard the garlic and set the oil aside until cool.

Place the garlic oil, pepper, cinnamon, salt, sugar, lemon juice
and soy sauce in a glass jar or bottle with a lid. Seal the jar and shake the
ingredients together. Set aside.

Toss the chickpeas, tomatoes and celery in a salad bowl. Shake
the dressing once more and pour over the salad. Toss in the chives and
sweet basil.

Serve with roasted chicken or barbecue meats.

SERVES 4–6

> Chickpeas come cooked in cans or dried in packets. If using
> dried chickpeas, soak overnight and cook in plenty of water for
> 1 to 2 hours depending on amount and how soft you like your
> chickpeas.
> The stock can be saved for use in other dishes. A cup of dry
> chickpeas can expand to 2 1/2 cups after soaking and cooking.
> Chickpeas are very rich in phytoestrogens, proteins and fibre.

BEAN SALAD

Cal : 685   kJ : 2845   Chol : 0 mg   Ca : 257 mg

1 x 440 g (14 oz) can three bean mix, about 240 g (8 oz) drained
1 cup (200 g, 7 oz) cooked soybeans *
150 g (5 oz) French or runner beans, ends trimmed
2 teaspoons (10 g, $1/2$ oz) red pepper, seeded and diced
2 teaspoons (10 g, $1/2$ oz) onions, finely diced
2 teaspoons sugar
$1/2$ teaspoon salt
$1/4$ teaspoon ground cinnamon
$1/4$ teaspoon ground nutmeg
$1/4$ teaspoon ground black pepper
4 tablespoons French salad dressing

Drain the three bean mix and wash with cool boiled water, then mix through the cooked soybeans.

Blanch the French beans in some salted, boiling water for 3 minutes. Quickly refresh in cold water, drain and cut into 2 cm ($3/4$ in) lengths. Add to the bean mixture.

Add the remaining ingredients and store in the refrigerator until ready to use, tossing a few times in order to mix the salad thoroughly with the dressing.

Serve cold with barbecued meats or cold meats.
SERVES 4–6

Note: If you are a diabetic, substitute the sugar with artificial sweetener.

* Precooked Soybeans
Dried soybeans can be cooked in a pressure cooker well ahead of time and stored in the refrigerator.
Soak 2 cups (400 g, 13 oz) soybeans overnight in cold water. Rinse and discard any bad beans or debri before cooking in a pressure cooker with $31/4$ cups (800 mL, 26 fl oz) water for 30 minutes. If cooking in ordinary saucepan, boil the soybeans for at least 3 hours after soaking.

APPLE AND POTATO SALAD

Cal : 735   kJ : 3040   Chol : 34 mg   Ca : 81 mg

500 g (1 lb) small or new potatoes
1 large green apple
1 tablespoon lime juice
20 g (3/4 oz) ham, diced
4–5 stalks fresh chives, snipped
100 g (3 1/2 oz) celery, fairly thinly sliced
5 tablespoons mayonnaise (low-fat or tofu (see page 49))
1 level teaspoon salt
freshly ground black pepper

Scrub potatoes, removing any eyes or dirt. Do not peel. Bring to the boil and cook for 12 minutes in a saucepan half-filled with water. Drain and allow to cool.

Wash and core the apple, but do not remove the skin. Cut into 1–2 cm (1/2–3/4 in) cubes and immediately mix with the lime juice. This process is called acidulation and helps prevent the apple from discolouring. Leave in the refrigerator.

Cool the potatoes and cut into 1–2 cm (1/2–3/4 in) chunks. Mix the ham with the potatoes. Add the chives and celery.

Mix in the mayonnaise, a few grindings of pepper and the acidulated apples. Leave to marinate in the refrigerator for an hour or so before serving.
SERVES 6–8

Apples contain estrone, which is a natural estrogen found circulating in the blood of post-menopausal women. Other foods such as rice also contain estrone, as well as estradiol. The latter is predominantly found circulating in the blood of pre-menopausal women.
Pomegranates contain estrone, too, hence the Chinese nickname of the 'fertility fruit'.

GADO GADO

Cal : 1273   kJ : 5347   Chol : 0 mg   Ca : 555 mg

1 tablespoon soybean oil
300 g (10 oz) hard tofu, cut into cubes
100 g (3^1/$_2$ oz) tempeh, sliced
2 tablespoons hot water
3 tablespoons *kecap manis* (sweet soy sauce made in Indonesia)
2 teaspoon finely diced garlic
2 tablespoons chilli sauce
4 tablespoons crushed roasted peanuts
200 g (7 oz) yam bean (jicama)
1 x 340 g (11 oz) can pineapple pieces
2 medium tomatoes
2 cucumbers
250 g (8 oz) mung bean shoots

Heat the soybean oil in nonstick frying pan or skillet. Fry the tofu and tempeh until the skin is brown and crispy. Drain on absorbent kitchen paper or paper towels.

Mix the hot water, soy sauce, garlic, chilli sauce and peanuts in a soup or small serving bowl. This is the gado gado sauce.

Peel the the yam bean and cut into strips like potato chips or thick-cut French fries. Cut the pineapple, tomatoes and cucumbers into bite-size chunks.

Boil some water and blanch the mung bean shoots for a minute. Drain well and arrange the yam bean, pineapple, tomatoes, cucumber and mung bean shoots on a platter with the tofu and tempeh.

Serve cold accompanied by the gado gado sauce. Each person chooses a selection from the platter, then pours some of the gado gado sauce over the top.

SERVES 6–8

Note: This dish goes well with coconut-flavoured rice and fish, or plain rice with dry curried beef (rendang).

THAI SALAD

Cal : 578   kJ : 2394   Chol : 0 mg   Ca : 145 mg

Dressing
1 tablespoon chopped fresh coriander (Chinese parsley) leaves
1 clove garlic, finely diced
2 tablespoons lime juice
1 tablespoon apple cider vinegar
3 tablespoons nam pla (fish sauce)
1 small red chilli pepper, diced
2 tablespoons boiling water
3 teaspoons sugar
$1/2$ teaspoon salt
2 teaspoons olive oil

Thai Salad
150 g (5 oz) lettuce, rinsed and drained
75 g ($2^1/_2$ oz) cucumber
40 g (1 $^1/_2$ oz) red capsicum (sweet pepper)
60 g (2 oz) fresh bean shoots, rinsed and drained
100 g (3 $^1/_2$ oz) fried tofu cubes (tofu buk)
100 g ($3^1/_2$ oz) cherry tomatoes, rinsed and drained
fresh coriander (Chinese parsley) leaves, to garnish
2 tablespoons roasted peanuts, peeled, to garnish

Blend all the ingredients for the dressing in a food processor. Set aside in the refrigerator until ready to use. (This quantity makes about $2/_3$ cup (150 mL, 5 fl oz) of dressing.)

To make the salad, tear the lettuce into smaller, bite-size portions. Cut the cucumber into chunks with the skin on, shred the capsicum and remove the stringy tails from the bean shoots. Cut the fried tofu cubes into quarters and slice the cherry tomatoes into halves if desired.

Arrange the salad vegetables in a dish or platter, and garnish with the fresh coriander leaves.

Crush the roasted peanuts and sprinkle on top of the salad just before serving. Pour over the dressing and serve immediately.

SERVES 4

POACHED SPICY
CHICKEN MARYLAND

Cal : 1028   kJ : 4301   Chol : 414 mg   Ca : 117 mg

4 cups (1 litre, 1³/₄ imp. pints) water
scant 1 cup (200 mL, 7 fl oz) light soy sauce
scant 1 cup (200 mL, 7 fl oz) dark soy sauce
1 tablespoon sugar
2 cloves garlic
2 pieces licorice root
1 stick cinnamon
1 star anise
10 black peppercorns
1 tablespoon oyster sauce
1 tablespoon white wine
2 cm (³/₄ in) piece of fresh ginger
4 pieces chicken Maryland (thigh with leg still attached)

Bring all the ingredients except the chicken to the boil in a medium-size saucepan. Allow to boil for 5 minutes.

Trim any visible fat off the chicken and discard. Pat the chicken dry with absorbent kitchen paper or a clean cloth.

Gently lower the chicken into the boiling stock. Allow to cook until the stock reaches the boil once again, then turn off the heat, cover with lid and let stand for 15 minutes on top of the stove or cooker.

Turn the chicken pieces over in the saucepan and once again bring to the simmer until just boiling. Turn off the heat once more and let stand for another 15 minutes.

Test to see whether the chicken is cooked by inserting a fork into the meaty part of the thigh. If it is cooked, the juices will run clear and not be tinged with any pinkness.

Serve hot with potatoes or steamed rice. Garnish with sliced cucumber, tomatoes and parsley, if desired.
SERVES 4

Note: The stock can be made ahead of time and frozen until you are ready to use. Simply thaw and continue with the recipe as above. Beef can be used instead of chicken. You can also use other parts or cuts of chicken, such as wings, thighs or breast fillets, but the energy, cholesterol and calcium levels will vary from those given above.

Licorice has very potent anti-flushing effects. It can be used in infusion as a beverage. The root is quite sweet and comes in slices packed in plastic bags.
Licorice root should not be used by people suffering from high blood pressure.

STEAMED TOFU AND EGGS

Cal : 580   kJ: 2436   Chol : 616 mg   Ca : 816 mg

1 tablespoon diced red onion
1 teaspoon oil
150 g (5 oz) tofu
150 g (5 oz) fish paste
$1/4$ teaspoon salt
freshly ground black pepper, to taste
2 large eggs, beaten
fresh chives or green part of spring onion, finely sliced, to garnish

Saute the onion in the oil until it is translucent and starting to brown.
Mash the tofu in a deep dish and mix well with the fish paste. Add the salt, pepper to taste, cooked onion and eggs.
Place the dish and its contents on a rack over boiling water and steam slowly for 25 minutes.
Sprinkle with the chives and serve hot with rice and stir-fried or steamed vegetables as side dishes.
SERVES 4

Note: Minced (ground) pork or beef can be used instead of fish paste. The pork will need longer steaming time unless it has been precooked.

STEWED BEAN CURD STICKS AND WOOD FUNGUS

Cal : 820   kJ : 3445   Chol : 126 mg   Ca : 161 mg

20 g ($^3/_4$ oz) wood fungus (cloud ear)
100 g ($3^1/_2$ oz) bean curd sticks (bamboo yuba)
200 g (7 oz) pork ribs
1 tablespoon white wine
2 tablespoons dark soy sauce
2 tablespoons red fermented bean curd
$^1/_4$ teaspoon sugar
freshly ground black pepper, to taste
1 tablespoon oil
4 cloves garlic, diced
1$^1/_4$ cups (310 mL, 10 fl oz) water
$^1/_2$ teaspoon cornflour (cornstarch)
fresh coriander (Chinese parsley) leaves, to garnish

Soak the wood fungus in hot water and remove any debris. Change the water if necessary. If not already shredded when bought, cut the fungus into smaller pieces after soaking for 30 minutes.

Break the bean curd sticks into 4–5 cm (1$^3/_4$–2 in) lengths and soak in hot water separately.

Cut the pork into bite-size portions and marinate with the wine, dark soy sauce, fermented bean curd, sugar and black pepper to taste.

Heat the oil in a heavy-based saucepan and add the garlic. Sauté until fragrant, then add the marinated pork and allow the meat to brown.

Drain the wood fungus and bean curd sticks, discarding the water. Add the fungus and bean curd to the saucepan. Sauté for 5 minutes before adding 1 cup (250 mL, 8 fl oz) of the water. Bring to the boil, then reduce the heat slightly and allow the stew to simmer for 40 minutes.

Mix the cornflour with the remaining $^1/_4$ cup (60 mL, 2 fl oz) water and add to the stew 5 minutes before the end of the cooking time. Stir through thoroughly.

Serve hot garnished with the coriander and accompanied by steamed rice.

SERVES 4–6

Wood fungus is also known as wood ear, cloud ear and tree ear. An albino form of this mushroom is called silver ear. Wood fungus comes in dehydrated form in packets obtainable from Asian food stores and some large supermarkets. It is available pre-shredded or whole, and has to be soaked in hot water before use. It swells five to six times in size, and resembles an ear after reconstituing, hence the common names. Wood fungus is reputed to possess anti-coagulation properties which decrease the stickiness of the platelets in the blood. Bean curd sticks are known as *bamboo yuba* in some countries. The protein content varies greatly between the various brands of this product.

SOYBEAN SHOOTS WITH MINCED PORK

Cal : 590   kJ : 2443   Chol : 60 mg   Ca : 68 mg

400 g (13 oz) soybean shoots
100 g (3^1/$_2$ oz) minced (ground) pork
1 teaspoon dark soy sauce
1 tablespoon light soy sauce
1 tablespoon oyster sauce
1 teaspoon white wine
1 tablespoon soybean oil
2 cloves garlic, diced
1 teaspoon cornflour (cornstarch)
^{1}/$_3$ cup (90 mL, 3 fl oz) water or stock
^{1}/$_4$ teaspoon salt
2 pinches of black pepper
fresh red chilli pepper or green spring onion
or coriander leaves, to garnish

Wash the soybean shoots and separate the white root from the yellow cotyledons, removing any stringy end roots. Chop up the yellow cotyledons and drain the white roots. Set aside.

Marinate the pork in the dark soy sauce, 1 teaspoon of the light soy sauce, 1 teaspoon of the oyster sauce and wine.

Heat 2 teaspoons of the soybean oil in wok over high heat. Sauté half of the garlic until brown. Stir in the white soy roots and the remaining 3 teaspoons light soy sauce. Add half of water and cook for 1 minute. Transfer to a serving plate, spreading over the plate evenly.

Reheat the wok and add the remaining 2 teaspoons oil and the remaining garlic. Add the marinated pork and stir-fry for 3 minutes, before adding the yellow cotyledons from the soybean shoots. Stir well, adding in the remaining 2 teaspoons oyster sauce, salt and pepper.

Cover and allow to cook for 2 minutes. Meanwhile, mix the cornflour with the remaining water. Stir into the stir-fried pork, mixing well, and cook for further 1–2 minutes before transferring to top of the cooked soy roots.

Garnish with red chillies or green shallots or coriander leaves, and serve.

SERVES 4

Note: This dish goes well with salads, noodles and steamed rice.

CURRIED TOFU AND VEGETABLES

Cal : 1030   kJ : 4324   Chol : 0 mg   Ca : 431 mg

1 tablespoon soybean oil
3 tablespoons diced onion or $^1/_2$ large onion, diced
2 cm ($^3/_4$ in) piece of fresh ginger, diced
1 tablespoon curry powder
1$^1/_4$ cup (310 mL, 10 fl oz) water
300 g (10 oz) pumpkin, peeled and cut into 2–3 cm ($^3/_4$–1 in) cubes
200 g (7 oz) green (French or runner) beans, trimmed and cut into 3–4 cm
(1–1$^1/_4$ in) lengths
200 g (7 oz) fried tofu
1 eggplant (aubergine), about 200–300 g (7–10 oz), cut into 2–3 cm
($^3/_4$–1 in) cubes
2 candle nuts, ground
4 tablespoons coconut powder
1 teaspoon chicken stock powder
$^1/_2$ teaspoon salt

Heat the soybean oil in a medium saucepan over a medium heat. Sauté the onion and ginger for 2 minutes.

Meanwhile, mix the curry powder and $^1/_4$ cup (60 mL, 2 fl oz) of the water into a paste. Add to the onion mixture and sauté for another 2–3 minutes, or until very fragrant.

Add the pumpkin and stir for few minutes before adding the green beans, tofu and eggplant. Add the remaining 1 cup (250 mL, 8 fl oz) water and the candle nut, coconut powder, chicken stock and salt. Simmer for 20–25 minutes. Serve hot with rice, bread or noodles.
SERVES 4–6

Note: Fresh shelled and deveined prawns (shrimp) can be added 8–10 minutes before the end of the cooking time if desired.

The best result is obtained with ready-fried tofu, which is sold in packets in Asian food stores or oriental markets. Fried tofu is light brown in colour and rather spongy in texture.

STEAMED RICE

Cal : 1428 kJ : 5880 Chol : 0 mg Ca : 28 mg

2 cups (400 g, 10 oz) short-grain rice
2 cups (500 mL, 16 fl oz) cold water

Wash the rice in a mixing bowl unless specified to the contrary on the packet, as some rice may be fortified and washing removes the additives.

Place the washed rice in a deep saucepan with a tight-fitting lid. Add the cold water, cover and bring to the boil over a high heat. Once boiling, lower the heat to medium and half-cover the saucepan with the lid.

When nearly all the water has been absorbed, turn the heat to the lowest possible setting on your stove or cooker. Cover the saucepan tightly with the lid once again and let stand for 15–20 minutes before serving.

SERVES 4–6

Microwave Rice: If you wish to cook rice in the microwave, wash the rice as before to remove any dust or other impurities. Place the rice in a microwave-proof ceramic dish of at least 10 cup- (2.5-litre, 4 imp. pint) capacity and add 2 cups (500 mL, 16 fl oz) boiling water. Cover and microwave on high for 8 minutes, then give the rice a stir before cooking on medium for 10 minutes. Let stand for 5 minutes before serving.

Most Asian restaurants serve long-grain fragrant jasmine rice. Basmati rice, which is also fragrant, is available from supermarkets and can be used for the Fried Rice recipe given on page 76. However, it is used more frequently in Indian cooking and goes very well with curries.

Rice does contain lignans, but not in as great a quantity as found in legumes. Estrone and estradiol are also present in rice.

It is essential not to cook rice in too much water. Otherwise, when you discard the excess water after cooking the rice, much of the nutrients will be lost.

FRIED RICE

Cal : 2315   kJ : 9559   Chol : 410 mg   Ca : 227 mg

1 large egg
a pinch of salt
freshly ground black pepper, to taste
2 tablespoons soybean oil
1 tablespoon diced onion
120 g (4 oz) barbecued pork (char siew), cut into $^1/_2$ cm ($^1/_4$ in) cubes
1 cup (150 g, 5 oz) frozen green peas, rinsed and drained
6 cups (400 g, 14 oz) cooked rice
3 tablespoons light soy sauce
3 cooked prawns (shrimp), peeled, deveined and diced (optional)
1 medium carrot, shredded
1 tablespoon oyster sauce
fresh coriander (Chinese parsley) leaves, to garnish (optional)

Beat the egg with the salt and pepper to taste.

Heat $^1/_2$ tablespoon of the soybean oil in a wok over a medium heat. When the oil is hot, add the beaten egg and spread the egg over the bottom of the wok as if cooking a thin crêpe. When the egg is just cooked, remove from the pan — do not overcook the egg as this will make it rubbery. Allow to cool before cutting into strips of 2–3 cm ($^3/_4$–1 in) long. Set aside.

Heat the remaining $1^1/_2$ tablespoons soybean oil in the wok. Add the onion and sauté until fragrant and just starting to brown.

Add the pork and green peas, and stir-fry for 1 minute. Add the rice and mix well, stirring constantly. Add the soy sauce and oyster sauce, and mix well.

Cook for another 5 minutes, then make a hollow in the middle of the rice before adding the prawns (if using) and carrot. Continue stir-frying for another 5 minutes.

Add the shredded egg and mix through the fried rice well. Garnish with the coriander leaves (if using) and serve hot.

SERVES 4–6

STIR-FRIED RICE VERMICELLI

Cal : 1124   kJ : 4719   Chol : 292 mg   Ca : 356 mg

250 g (8 oz) rice vermicelli
2 spring onions
2 cloves garlic
1 large egg
$1/2$ teaspoon salt
pinch of ground black pepper
2 tablespoons soybean oil
100 g (3$1/2$ oz) tofu cutlet, cut into strips
100 g (3$1/2$ oz) fish cake, cut into strips
250 g (8 oz) bean shoots, rinsed and drained
2 tablespoons oyster sauce
3 tablespoons light soy sauce

Soak the rice vermicelli in lukewarm water for 10 minutes. Separate the strains before draining. Wash the spring onions. Dice the white portion of the spring onion with the garlic. Cut the green stems of the spring onion into 3–4 cm (1$1/4$ in) lengths. Set aside.

Beat the egg with the salt and pepper. Heat 1 teaspoon of the soybean oil in a wok over a medium heat. When the oil is hot, add the beaten egg and spread the egg over the bottom of the wok as if cooking a thin crêpe. When the egg is just cooked, remove from the pan — do not overcook the egg as this will make it rubbery. Allow to cool before cutting into strips of 2–3 cm (3/4–1 in) long. Set aside.

Heat the remaining soybean oil in the wok and stir-fry diced garlic and spring onion until light brown. Add the tofu cutlet and fish cake. Stir-fry gently before adding the oyster sauce and 1 teaspoon of the light soy sauce. Add the rice vermicelli and the remaining light soy sauce, and stir-fry over a high heat, stirring constantly, for 7–8 minutes.

Make a depression in the centre of the rice vermicelli and add the bean shoots. Check the seasoning and add more salt and pepper if desired. Stir-fry for 4–5 minutes.

Add the cooked egg and green spring onion stems. Mix well and serve immediately.

SERVES 4

SOYBEAN VINDALOO

Cal : 780   kJ : 3248   Chol : 104 mg   Ca : 253 mg

150 g (5 oz) minced (ground) chicken meat
1 tablespoon light soy sauce
2 cloves garlic, diced
1 tablespoon soybean oil
1 tablespoon diced onion
1 cm ($1/2$ in) piece of fresh ginger, chopped
2 teaspoons ground cumin
2 teaspoons ground mustard seeds
$1/2$ teaspoon ground turmeric
2 teaspoons water
4 medium red chilli peppers, seeded and finely chopped
400 g (14 oz) pressure-cooked soybeans
2 tablespoons soybean stock
$1/2$ teaspoon sugar
1 teaspoon salt
1–2 tablespoons apple cider vinegar

Marinate the chicken in the soy sauce.

Sauté the garlic in the soybean oil in a deep saucepan over a medium heat. When the garlic is light brown, add the onion and ginger. Sauté for 2–3 minutes, stirring regularly.

Make a paste of the cumin, mustard seeds and turmeric with the water. Add this and the chilli peppers to the paste in the saucepan and sauté until fragrant.

Now add the marinated chicken and stir-fry for 3 minutes before adding the soybeans, stock, sugar and salt. Reduce the heat to very low and simmer for 10 minutes.

Add the apple cider vinegar, stirring through well, and simmer for further 3–4 minutes. Serve hot with rice and vegetable salad. This curry can also be used as a filling for taco shells or pasties.

SERVES 3–4

Small chilli peppers are extremely hot; the medium-size ones less so. The chilli peppers used in this recipe should be the size of your little finger.

STUFFED FRIED TOFU CUBES

Cal : 1011   kJ : 4245   Chol : 128 mg   Ca : 1347 mg

small bunch of fresh coriander
2 cloves garlic
75 g (2^1/$_2$ oz) minced (ground) pork
150 g (5 oz) fresh fish paste
^{1}/$_8$ teaspoon five-spice powder
1 ^{1}/$_2$ teaspoons cornflour (cornstarch)
1 tablespoon plus ^{1}/$_2$ teaspoon oyster sauce
1 packet or about 190 g (7 oz) fried tofu cubes (tofu buk)
1 tablespoon oil
1 tablespoon dark soy sauce
^{2}/$_3$ cup (150 mL, 5 fl oz) water

Rinse the coriander and dice up 1 clove of the garlic together with
2 stalks of the coriander.

Thoroughly combine the pork, fish paste, five-spice powder,
^{1}/$_2$ teaspoon of the cornflour and ^{1}/$_2$ teaspoon of the oyster sauce.

Wash the tofu cubes and cut each cube in half. Stuff a little of the
pork mixture into the top of each tofu half and smooth over the top.

Heat the oil in a wok over a medium heat. Dice the remaining
clove of garlic and stir-fry in the oil until brown and fragrant. Carefully add
the stuffed tofu cubes to the wok, with the stuffed side down. Cook for
5 minutes.

Add the remaining 1 tablespoon oyster sauce and the dark soy
sauce to the wok. Mix the remaining 1 teaspoon cornflour with the water
and pour into the wok. Simmer on a very low heat for a further
20 minutes. Serve hot garnished with some fresh coriander leaves and
accompanied by plain steamed rice and steamed vegetables.
SERVES 4–5

Note: Fish paste is available from Asian food stores or oriental markets.
Mackerel fillets or cutlets can be used in place of the fish paste, but
ensure that all bones are removed. Chop up finely before mixing the
mackerel with the rest of the ingredients.

FRENCH BEAN OMELETTE

Cal : 607   kJ : 2513   Chol : 1050 mg   Ca : 194 mg

200 g (7 oz) French (green or string) beans
4 large eggs
$1/2$ teaspoon salt
freshly ground black pepper, to taste
1 clove garlic, finely diced
1 tablespoon soybean oil

Rinse the beans and remove the ends. Slice into thin rounds.

Beat the eggs with $1/4$ teaspoon of the salt and pepper to taste. Set aside.

Heat $1/2$ tablespoon of the oil in a wok or saucepan until nearly smoking. Add the garlic and stir well. Add the beans and the remaining $1/4$ teaspoon salt. Cook for about 3 minutes before reducing the heat to medium.

Transfer the cooked beans to the egg mixture and stir through well. Pour half the egg and bean mixture into the wok or saucepan, and spread the mixture out to form an omelette. Cook for a minute before turning the omelette over.

Heat the remaining $1/2$ tablespoon oil in the wok and cook the remaining egg and bean mixture as before.

Serve immediately with steamed rice or pasta salad.

SERVES 2–4 (MAKES 2 LARGE OMELETTES)

Note: Use 2 scramblers (egg substitute) with 2 eggs in order to reduce the cholesterol content of this recipe by half. If desired you can make smaller omelettes by dividing the mixture into smaller portions before cooking each omelette individually.

French beans contain phytoestrogens. The amount varies
according to harvesting, growth conditions and the variety.
The fresh round variety is very tasty and cooks quite quickly.
Long green beans, otherwise known as snake beans, can also
be used in this recipe.

WHEAT NOODLES
WITH TOFU CUTLET

Cal : 1673   kJ : 7028   Chol : 178 mg   Ca : 314 mg

1 packet (350 g, 11 oz) fresh wheat noodles
250 g (8 oz) bean shoots, rinsed and drained
2 tablespoons soybean oil
3 cloves garlic, diced
100 g (3$^1/_2$ oz) barbecue pork (char siew), thinly sliced
100 g (3$^1/_2$ oz) tofu cutlets, thinly sliced
3 tablespoons oyster sauce
3 tablespoons light soy sauce
1 tablespoon sesame oil

Bring plenty of water to the boil in a large saucepan. Add half of the
noodles and cook for 1–2 minutes, until quite transparent instead of being
opaque. Remove the noodles from the water and plunge into cold water
for 2 minutes before draining. Cook the second half of noodles in the
same way, then drain.

Discard the cooking water and place 4 cups (1 litre, 1$^3/_4$ imp.
pints) hot water in the saucepan. Blanch the bean shoots when the water
is boiling rapidly (30 seconds is enough). Drain well and set aside. Do not
discard the hot water.

Heat the soybean oil in a separate saucepan and sauté the garlic
until fragrant. Remove three-quarters of the contents of the pan and
reserve. Now add the pork, tofu, 1 tablespoon of the soy sauce and
1 tablespoon of the oyster sauce to the pan. Mix well and remove from
the heat.

Return the noodles to the saucepan of hot water for 30 seconds.
Drain the noodles and discard the cooking water, then mix the noodles
with the sesame oil, the reserved garlic mixture and remaining
2 tablespoons of oyster sauce and 2 tablespoons of light soy sauce.

Divide the noodles between 4 serving dishes. Arrange the bean
shoots and pork mixture on top. Serve warm or hot.
SERVES 4

BAKED STUFFED PUMPKIN

Using block cheese
Cal : 656   kJ : 2743   Chol : 83 mg   Ca : 833 mg
Using soy cheese
Cal : 636   kJ : 2673   Chol : 0 mg   Ca : 628 mg

1 Japanese pumpkin, 20–25 cm (8–10 in) in diameter, halved
$^1/_2$ teaspoon chicken stock powder
100–125 g (3$^1/_2$–4 oz) cauliflower, cut into florets
75–100 g (2$^1/_2$–3$^1/_2$ oz) broccoli, cut into florets
200 g (7 oz) mushrooms, sliced
4–5 slices of leek, cut 1 cm ($^1/_2$ in) thick (optional)
scant 1 cup (100 g, 3$^1/_2$ oz) grated cheese or chive-flavoured soy cheese

Preheat the oven to 160°C (325°F).

Wash the pumpkin and scoop out the seeds. Do not peel. Score the inside flesh with a knife. Cover the pumpkin halves with plastic wrap and cook on high for 6 minutes in the microwave.

Scoop some flesh out of the centre of each pumpkin half, leaving a shell of flesh 2–3 cm ($^3/_4$–1 in) thick. Reserve the scooped-out flesh for making pumpkin soup later.

Rub the inside of each pumpkin shell with the chicken stock. Pack the cauliflower, broccoli, mushrooms and leek (if using) neatly into each pumpkin half and sprinkle the cheese over the top.

Bake in the oven for 30 minutes.

Cut into four to six portions and serve hot with a light meat dish.
SERVES 4–6

Japanese pumpkin is quite sweet and very tasty. The skin is very pretty with yellow and green patterns and looks attractive when cooked. Japanese pumpkin tends to be smaller than many other varieties.
Too much pumpkin too often may cause a condition known as carotenemia, which turns the skin and palms an orange colour. Young females with carotenemia can lose their menses (periods) for months.

TERIYAKI CHICKEN

Cal : 696   kJ : 2915   Chol : 276 mg   Ca : 49 mg

400 g (14 oz) chicken thigh fillet
$1/4$ teaspoon sugar
pinch of salt
4 tablespoons teriyaki sauce
1 tablespoon sesame oil, for basting
lettuce leaves, to garnish

Remove any visible fat from the chicken fillet and discard. Slice the fillet into strips 2 cm ($3/4$ in) thick and place in a bowl.

Sprinkle the sugar and salt over the top of the chicken and mix in well. Add the teriyaki sauce and leave to marinate in the refrigerator for at least 30 minutes.

Cook under a hot grill or broiler, turning the chicken after 5 minutes. Baste with any remaining marinade and the sesame oil.

Serve hot on a bed of lettuce leaves.

SERVES 2–4

Note: This dish goes very well with rice and stir-fried or steamed vegetables. Other accompaniments such as raw vegetable salads or pickled radish, ginger and carrots can be served with the rice.

Chicken breast fillet can be used instead of thigh fillet;
it has much less visible fat.
Fish fillets can be used in place of chicken meat. However, fish
will cook more quickly than the chicken so take care
not to overcook.
Teriyaki sauce is made from soybeans and also contains wine,
wheat and spices.

STIR-FRIED CHINESE CABBAGE AND BEAN VERMICELLI

Cal : 710   kJ : 2980   Chol : 89 mg   Ca : 101 mg

50 g (2 oz) bean vermicelli (cellophane vermicelli)
100 g (3 1/2 oz) minced (ground) pork
2 teaspoons white wine
2 tablespoons oyster sauce
1 tablespoon light soy sauce
freshly ground black pepper, to taste
1/2 small Chinese cabbage
2 cloves garlic, diced
2 tablespoons soybean oil
1 medium carrot, shredded
1/4 teaspoon salt
1 teaspoon cornflour (cornstarch)
1/2 cup (125 mL, 4 fl oz) water

Soak the bean vermicelli in cold water for 20 minutes, then cut into 10–15cm (4–6 in) lengths. Drain well and set aside.

Marinate the pork in the wine, 1 tablespoon of the oyster sauce, light soy sauce and pepper to taste for 15–20 minutes.

Rinse the Chinese cabbage and cut into bite–size pieces about 1 cm (1/2 in) in width. Drain well.

Heat the soybean oil in a wok and stir-fry the garlic until fragrant before adding the marinated pork. Stir-fry for 4–5 minutes.

Add the Chinese cabbage and stir-fry for 2–3 minutes. Add the carrot and bean vermicelli. Stir through well and cook for a further 3–4 minutes. Add remaining 1 tablespoon oyster sauce and the salt.

Mix the cornflour with the water and add to the wok. Cook for 2 minutes before removing to a serving dish.

Serve with steamed rice and other stir-fried vegetables.

SERVES 4–6

Bean vermicelli is made from mung bean flour and is rich in proteins and vitamin B. It also contains phytoestrogens. Bean vermicelli can be used in soups.

ROASTED SPICY CHICKEN MARYLAND

Cal : 504   kJ: 2125   Chol : 276 mg   Ca : 43 mg

2 pieces of chicken Maryland (thigh with leg attached)
2 tablespoons light soy sauce
$1/2$ teaspoon dried sage
1 teaspoon ground fennel
$1/2$ teaspoon ground cinnamon
$1/4$ teaspoon star anise powder
$1/4$ teaspoon ground black pepper
$1/2$ teaspoon sugar
2 cloves garlic, finely chopped

Remove any visible fat from the chicken Maryland. Pat the chicken dry with absorbent kitchen paper.

Place the chicken in a container suitable for marinating and add the remaining ingredients. Marinate in the refrigerator for at least 4 hours or preferably overnight, turning the chicken pieces occasionally so that all sides are well marinated.

Preheat the oven to 160°C (325°F). Roast the marinated chicken in a roasting pan on a rack for 40 minutes. Baste the skin at least once during the roasting time with the remaining marinade.

Serve hot with vegetables and noodles.

SERVES 2

Note: The chicken can be barbecued, but make sure that it is well cooked as the drumstick is rather thick and takes longer to cook than other parts of the chicken.

Sage, cinnamon and fennel all contain estrogen.
Soy sauce is made from fermented soybeans and contains very small quantites of natural estrogens.
The oil and fat in this dish are drained during cooking if the chicken is roasted on a rack. However, if you wish to reduce the fat content of this dish even further, remove the skin on the chicken before marinating.

SESAME CHICKEN FILLET

Cal : 1031   kJ : 4309   Chol : 345 mg   Ca : 144 mg

500 g (1 lb) chicken thigh fillet
1 tablespoon dry sherry
1 tablespoon light soy sauce
1 tablespoon oyster sauce
1 tablespoon tahini
3 cm (1$^1/_4$ in) piece of fresh ginger
2 teaspoons sesame oil
2 tablespoons sesame seeds
$^1/_4$ teaspoon salt
1 clove garlic, diced

Trim any visible fat off the chicken and discard. Cut the chicken into bite-size chunks. Place the chicken, sherry, light soy sauce, oyster sauce and tahini in a bowl or other suitable dish, and marinate in the refrigerator for 1 hour.

Scrape the skin off the ginger, then thinly slice the ginger root.

Heat the sesame oil in a wok over a medium heat and stir-fry the ginger until fragrant.

Increase the heat and stir-fry the marinated chicken for 15 minutes, or until no moist sauce is left in the wok.

Reduce the heat slightly before adding the sesame seeds. The sesame seeds need to be stir-fried over a medium heat so that they do not burn too quickly or jump out of the wok.

Serve with steamed vegetables and rice.

SERVES 2–4

This dish is tradtionally cooked for new mothers during the month of confinement, but with lots more fresh ginger than given in this recipe, which has been adapted for the family. The nutritional and estrogen content helps to buffer the rapid plunge in the body's estrogen level which occurs after delivery of a baby. Phytoestrogens are present in whole sesame seeds, sesame oil and tahini.
Fresh ginger contains a natural anti-coagulant which helps prevent deep venous thrombosis and pulmonary embolism.

CHICKEN AND POTATO CURRY

Cal : 1413   kJ : 5933   Chol : 345 mg   Ca : 540 mg

500 g (1 lb) chicken thigh fillet
1 tablespoon oil
2 cloves garlic, diced
$^1/_2$ medium onion, diced
3 slices of fresh ginger, minced
3 candle nuts, crushed
1 tablespoon curry powder
scant $^1/_2$ cup (100 mL, $3^1/_2$ fl oz) lukewarm water
10 curry leaves (optional)
1 stalk lemon grass (optional)
1 star anise
1 small stick cinnamon
$1^3/_4$ cups (400 mL, 14 fl oz) soy milk
1 teaspoon sugar
1 teaspoon salt
400 g (14 oz) potatoes, peeled and quartered
5 tablespoons coconut powder

Remove any visible fat from the chicken fillet and discard. Cut the chicken into 4–5 cm ($1^3/_4$–2 in) chunks.

Heat the oil in a heavy-based saucepan over a medium heat. Add the garlic and sauté until fragrant. Add the onion and ginger, and sauté for 2 minutes before adding the candle nuts.

Mix the curry powder and half the water into a paste. Add the curry paste to the pan, stirring well, and cook until fragrant, then stir through the curry leaves and lemon grass (if using).

Add the chicken pieces, star anise and cinnamon, and mix thoroughly before adding the soy milk, sugar and salt. Stir thoroughly, then add the potatoes.

Mix the coconut powder with the remaining water and stir into the curry. Cook for a further 20 minutes over a low heat. Serve hot with boiled rice.

SERVES 4

SHREDDED BEEF
WITH BEAN CURD

Cal : 802   kJ : 3345   Chol : 150 mg   Ca : 194 mg

250 g (8 oz) beef fillet or New York cut, sliced into thin strips
1 teaspoon sesame oil
1 teaspoon light soy sauce
pinch of ground black pepper
200 g (7 oz) fried tofu (tofu buk)
2 tablespoons cornflour (cornstarch)
soybean oil, for deep-frying
1 clove garlic, diced
2 medium carrots, peeled and cut into julienne

Sauce
2 teaspoons apple cider vinegar
1 teaspoon dry sherry
2 teaspoons soy sauce
$1/2$ cube beef stock
$1/4$ teaspoon salt
$1/2$ teaspoon sugar

Marinate the beef in the sesame oil, light soy sauce and pepper for
30 minutes. Cut the bean curd into strips and toss in $1/2$ tablespoon of the
cornflour. Add 1 tablespoon of the cornflour to the beef and toss well
before deep-frying in very hot soybean oil. Drain the beef well on
absorbent kitchen paper, then sprinkle the remaining $1/2$ tablespoon
cornflour onto the beef.

Pat the carrots dry with absorbent kitchen paper before deep-
frying until they float on top of the oil. Remove and drain on clean
absorbent kitchen paper.

Deep-fry the fried tofu strips and drain well.

To make the sauce, place the cider vinegar, dry sherry, soy sauce,
beef stock, salt and sugar in a clean saucepan. Bring to the boil, then add
the beef, carrot and fried tofu.

Serve hot with rice and steamed green vegetables.

SERVES 4

CURRIED CHICKPEAS

Cal : 654   kJ : 2749   Chol : 0 mg   Ca : 241 mg

200 g (7 oz) dried chickpeas (garbanzo beans)
pinch of bicarbonate of soda
100 g (3$^1/_2$ oz) tamarind paste
1$^3/_4$ cups (400 mL, 14 fl oz) water
2 tablespoons soybean oil
1 medium onion, peeled and chopped
4 cm (1$^3/_4$ in) piece of fresh ginger, finely grated
4 green chilli peppers, chopped
1 teaspoon salt
$^1/_4$ teaspoon red chilli powder
1$^1/_2$ teaspoons garam masala
2 lemons, thinly sliced, to garnish
$^1/_2$ cup coriander (Chinese parsley) leaves, chopped, to garnish

Rinse the chickpeas, discarding any bad ones. Soak the chickpeas overnight in cold water with the bicarbonate of soda.

Soak the tamarind in scant $^1/_2$ cup (100 mL, 3$^1/_2$ fl oz) of the water. Remove the seeds and pulp, and strain and reserve the juice for cooking.

Pressure-cook the chickpeas in the remaining 1$^1/_4$ cups (300 mL, 10 fl oz) water for 10 minutes (see box on page 90). Depressurise carefully and drain the chickpeas. Reserve the cooking water.

Heat the soybean oil in a deep frying pan or skillet. Add the onion and ginger, and sauté until brown, then add the green chilli peppers, salt, chilli powder, garam masala and the drained chickpeas. Sauté for a few minutes before adding the reserved tarmarind juice and the cooking water from the pressure cooker.

Simmer until the gravy becomes quite thick. Remove from the heat and transfer to a deep serving dish. Garnish with the lemon and coriander, and serve hot with steamed rice, pappadams or chapatis.
SERVES 4–6

Note: This dish is adapted from a recipe provided by Dr A. Gulati.

The chickpeas can be cooked in a heavy-based saucepan for
1 hour if you do not have a pressure cooker, although the latter
reduces cooking time significantly. If you own one, take
advantange of it by using it for fast cooking of pulses.
Omit steps one and three if you are using canned chickpeas
(use 1 x 400 g (13 oz) can).

STUFFED TOFU
WITH SOY CHEESE SAUCE

Cal : 1761   kJ : 7398   Chol : 137 mg   Ca : 1915 mg

2 cloves garlic, diced
1 tablespoon diced onion
2 teaspoons soybean oil
1$^3/_4$ cups (200 g, 7 oz) grated soy cheese, plus extra for topping
$^1/_2$ cup cooked brown rice
freshly ground black pepper, to taste
2 teaspoons light soy sauce
100 g (3$^1/_2$ oz) canned red salmon
$^1/_2$ level teaspoon salt
1 packet (190 g, 6 oz) fried tofu cubes
1 tablespoon hot water
$^2/_3$ cup (150 mL, 5 fl oz) milk
1 tablespoon butter or margarine
fresh chives, snipped (optional)
tomato wedges, to garnish
fresh parsley, to garnish

90

Pre-cook the brown rice either by the evaporation or microwave method (see page 75). Brown rice requires 20 per cent more water than white rice to cook.

Sauté the garlic and onion in the soybean oil until brown. Combine with half the soy cheese, brown rice, pepper to taste, soy sauce, red salmon and $1/4$ teaspoon of the salt.

Wash the fried tofu cubes and cut a cross on one surface of each cube. Divide the filling equally between the cubes and stuff into each piece of tofu.

Place in a microwave-proof ceramic dish and add the hot water before cooking in the microwave on high for 4 minutes.

Remove from the microwave and sprinkle some extra soy cheese on top of the tofu. Place the dish under a hot grill or broiler for 5 minutes. Garnish with tomatoes and fresh parsley, and serve with hot soy cheese sauce.

To make the soy cheese sauce, heat the butter or margarine in a saucepan. Add the remaining soy cheese and the milk. Stir well before adding the remaining $1/4$ teaspoon salt. Continue stirring, then remove from the heat when sauce is smooth. Add the chives (if using) and pour over the stuffed tofu or serve in a gravy boat as an accompaniment.
SERVES 3–4

Fried tofu cubes are brown in colour and about 2–3 cm ($3/4$–1 in) in diameter. They usually come in packs of twelve. Make sure they are very fresh before buying.

SOYBEAN SHOOTS
WITH SHREDDED BEEF

Cal : 450   kJ : 1865   Chol : 70 mg   Ca : 44 mg

100 g (3$^1/_2$ oz) beef fillet, cut into strips
2 cm ($^3/_4$ in) piece of fresh ginger, cut into fine julienne
1 tablespoon light soy sauce
1$^1/_2$ tablespoons oyster sauce
1 tablespoon white wine
pinch of ground black pepper
200 g (7 oz) soy sprouts
1 tablespoon soybean oil
2 cloves garlic, diced
1 teaspoon cornflour (cornstarch)
scant $^1/_3$ cup (90 mL, 3 fl oz) water or stock

Place the beef, ginger, soy sauce, $^1/_2$ tablespoon of the oyster sauce, wine and pepper in a bowl. Mix well and set aside to marinate.

Wash the soy sprouts and remove any unsightly tips or roots.

Heat $^1/_2$ tablespoon of the soybean oil in a wok over a high heat. Add half of the garlic and cook until just starting to brown. Add the bean shoots and stir-fry for a couple of minutes before adding the remaining 1 tablespoon oyster sauce. Cover the wok for 2 minutes

Mix the cornflour with half of the water. Add to the wok and continue to cook, uncovered, for a further 2 minutes. Transfer the bean shoot mixture to a serving plate.

Heat the remaining $^1/_2$ tablespoon soybean oil in the wok. Stir-fry the remaining garlic until light brown before adding the marinated beef.

Stir quickly for 2 minutes, then add the remaining water. Allow to cook, covered, for a further minute.

Transfer the shredded beef to the top of the cooked bean shoots and serve immediately.

SERVES 3–4

Note: This dish goes well with steamed rice or noodles.

SOYBEAN SHOOTS WITH PRAWNS

Cal : 482   kJ : 2012   Chol : 378 mg   Ca : 230 mg

200 g (7 oz) fresh prawns (shrimp), peeled and deveined
1 tablespoon soy sauce
1 tablespoon oyster sauce
1 teaspoon white wine
freshly ground black pepper, to taste
200 g (7 oz) soybean shoots
1 1/2 tablespoons canola or soybean oil
2 cloves garlic, diced
1/4 teaspoon salt
1 teaspoon cornflour (cornstarch)
2 tablespoons water
fresh coriander (Chinese parsley) leaves, to garnish

Marinate the prawns in the soy sauce, oyster sauce, wine and pepper to taste for 10 minutes.

Wash the soybean shoots and remove the tails if desired. Set aside to drain.

Heat the oil in a wok or frying pan, then add the garlic and stir-fry until fragrant. Add the prawns and the marinade. Cook for 2–3 minutes, then quickly remove the prawns from the wok and set aside on a plate.

Now add the soybean shoots to the wok, tossing frequently for about 5 minutes over a high heat. Add the salt during cooking.

Return the prawns to the wok and stir through well. Mix the cornflour into a paste with the water, then add to the wok.

Transfer to a serving plate when the sauce has thickened and garnish with fresh coriander. Serve hot with boiled rice.

SERVES 3–4

Soybean shoots are rich in vitamin C, phytic acid and phytoestrogens.
The bright yellow cotyledons contain most of the nutrients found in the bean itself, and are very crunchy in texture and rather nutty in flavour.

STEAMBOAT

Steamboat is particularly great for cold weather or for when you want to linger over a meal, chatting with your fellow diners in between the various courses, as the dishes are cooked before your very eyes at the dining table. It is not hard to set up.

A steamboat cooker on charcoal is traditionally used and is placed at the centre of the table with adequate insulation to prevent damage to your dining table. However, an electric rice cooker or electric wok will do just fine if you do not have a steamboat cooker. Special metal nets are used to fish out the cooked meats or vegetables from the stock in which the items are cooked. These steamboat nets are cheap and easily obtained from most Asian grocery stores or oriental markets, and are usually found in the crockery and cutlery section.

Seafood cooks quite quickly in rapidly boiling stock, while meats such as pork and chicken take longer. Pork takes the longest time to cook. Slicing the meats thinly will ensure shorter cooking time. All vegetables and the tofu listed in the recipe for steamboat cook very quickly. The bean vermicelli will take about twice as long as the vegetables to cook.

The various sauces are placed around the table in convenient locations for the diners to reach; some sauces go better with certain meats or vegetables. Suggestions of what goes with what follow:

FRAGRANT SOY SAUCE: Practically all the meats and vegetables listed in the recipe will go very well with this sauce.

OYSTER SAUCE: Meats and scallops go well with oyster sauce. Chinese cabbage, tofu, Chinese chrysanthemum and bean shoots also taste great with this.

LIME AND FISH SAUCE: Seafoods such as prawns (shrimp), fish and scallops are suggested for this sauce. Chicken is also suitable.

PLUM SAUCE: All meats will go well with this sauce. Perhaps surprisingly, fish tastes good with plum sauce, too.

HOI SIN SAUCE: This sauce goes very well with tofu and beef. Try it with squid and pork as well.

TOM YUM SAUCE: This hot and tangy sauce goes well with any of the meats and vegetables listed, if you do not mind the hotness on your tongue. I normally use it with the seafoods.

CHILLI SAUCE: This sauce will go well with any of the meats and seafoods. Bean shoots can be eaten with chilli sauce if you like your food hot.

SATAY PEANUT SAUCE: All the meats and vegetables will go with this sauce. However, some items such as squid, beef, chicken, bean shoots, tofu and prawns taste exceptionally delicious with this sauce.

You will notice that a calculation of the energy, cholesterol and calcium content for this recipe is not given. As this is a versatile dish in that you can use any combinations of vegetables, meats, sauces and seafoods, it becomes impossible to calculate the possible combination of ingredients you will use. In practical terms, the amounts of meat and vegetables, and so on, do not come in standard serving sizes. You simply select what you like to eat with whatever sauces you like and the amount that you like. Finally, leave enough room to drink the soup that remains in the cooker.

500 g (1 lb) fresh prawns (shrimp), peeled and deveined
300 g (10 oz) scallops
200 g (7 oz) pork fillet, very thinly sliced
200 g (7 oz) beef fillet, very thinly sliced
300 g (10 oz) chicken breast fillet, very thinly sliced
300 g (10 oz) squid, skinned and cut into bite-size pieces
300 g (10 oz) beef balls, halved
300 g (10 oz) fish balls, halved
fresh coriander leaves or similar, to garnish
100 g (3^1/$_2$ oz) bean vermicelli
50 g (2 oz) Chinese cabbage
1 bunch of Chinese chrysanthemum vegetable
1 bunch of young spring onions
250 g (8 oz) bean shoots
600 g (1^1/$_4$ lb) tofu
3–4 litres (3–4 quarts, 4^3/$_4$–6^1/$_2$ imp. pints) chicken stock

Wash and salt the prawns very lightly, then wash the scallops and drain, adding just a pinch of salt.

Arrange all the meat and seafood on a platter and garnish with coriander or similar herbs. Store in the refrigerator until ready to use.

Soak the bean vermicelli in cold water. Drain well before use. Rinse the Chinese cabbage and cut into bite-size pieces. Drain well.

Rinse and drain the Chinese chrysanthemum vegetable very well, as it usually has a lot of soil caught between the leaves.

Cut the spring onion into 3–4 cm ($1^1/_4$–$1^1/_2$ in) lengths and wash well. Rinse the bean shoots and trim the roots if necessary.

Arrange the vegetables and tofu on another platter with the bean vermicelli. Place on the table with the meat and seafood platter.

Pour 2–3 litres (2–3 quarts, $3^1/_4$–$4^3/_4$ imp. pints) of the stock into the steamboat cooker and bring to boil . Cook the items in the steamboat one group at a time to ensure complete and even cooking. For example, beef cooks faster than pork, and bean shoots cook faster than Chinese cabbage. Use the steamboat nets to remove the cooked items from the steamboat.

Eat while hot, dipping individual items in any of the sauces found below. Top the steamboat up with more stock if necessary.

SERVES 6–8

FRAGRANT SOY SAUCE

Sauté 1 tablespoon diced onion and 1 tablespoon diced garlic in 1 tablespoon soybean oil until golden brown. Add a pinch of sugar, 2 tablespoons hot water and $1/_3$ cup (90 mL, 3 fl oz) light soy sauce.

OYSTER SAUCE

Add 2 teaspoons sesame oil to 2 tablespoons good-quality oyster sauce, then mix with 3 teaspoons hot water.

LIME AND FISH SAUCE

Shred 3–4 young lime leaves and 1 red chilli pepper. Combine with 2 tablespoons fish sauce, 1 tablespoon lime juice, 1 teaspoon sugar and 2 tablespoons hot water.

PLUM SAUCE

Mix 1 tablespoon plum sauce with 1 tablespoon hot water and $1/_4$ teaspoon salt.

HOI SIN SAUCE

Mix 1 tablespoon hoi sin sauce with 5 teaspoons hot water and 1 teaspoon sesame oil.

Tom Yum Sauce

Mix 1 tablespoon tom yum paste with 2 tablespoons hot water,
2 teaspoons lime juice, $1/4$ teaspoon salt and 1 teaspoon sugar.

Chilli Sauce

Blend $1/2$ cup (50 g, 2 oz) hot chilli peppers, 2 cloves garlic, 1 teaspoon
chopped fresh ginger, 1 teaspoon sugar, $3/4$ teaspoon salt in $1^1/_2$–
2 tablespoons white vinegar. Alternatively use one of the commercial
brands of ready made chilli sauce.

Satay Peanut Sauce

Sauté 1 tablespoon diced garlic and 1 tablespoon diced onion in
1 tablespoon oil. Add 2 teaspoons curry powder mixed with
$1^1/_2$ tablespoons water. Add 2 finely crushed candle nuts and 6 curry
leaves. Sauté until fragrant, then add $1^1/_4$ cups (300 mL, 10 fl oz) water
and 3 tablespoons coconut powder, $1/2$ teaspoon chicken stock powder,
$1/2$ teaspoon lime juice and $1/2$ teaspoon sugar. Bring to the boil, then
remove from the heat and add $1/2$ cup (100 g, $3^1/_2$ oz) crushed peeled
roasted peanuts.

POTATO CASSEROLE IN TOFU SAUCE

Cal : 1190   kJ : 4998   Chol : 46 mg   Ca : 336 mg

1 kg (2 lb) potatoes
1 large rasher (slice) bacon, about 80 g (2 $^3/_4$ oz)
1 tablespoon soybean oil
200 g (7 oz) tofu
$^2/_3$ cup (150 mL, 5 fl oz) water
$^1/_2$ teaspoon salt
freshly ground black pepper, to taste
1 teaspoon French onion stock powder or chicken stock powder
1 tablespoon cornflour (cornstarch)
$^2/_3$ cup (150 mL, 5 fl oz) soy milk
chopped fresh parsley (optional)
sliced tomatoes (optional)
grated cheese (optional)

Preheat the oven to 180°C (350°F).

Peel the potatoes and cut into slices 3–4 mm ($^1/_8$ in) thick.

Remove any rind and fat from the bacon and discard. Cut the bacon into small pieces.

Put the soybean oil in a large, nonstick saucepan or deep frying pan over a medium heat. Add the bacon pieces and toss for 3–4 minutes. Add the potato slices and mix well with the bacon. Sauté for 5 minutes.

Blend the tofu in a scant $^1/_2$ cup (100 mL, 3$^1/_2$ fl oz) of the water and add this to the pan. Add the salt, pepper to taste and French onion stock.

Mix the cornflour with the remaining water. Add this to thicken the sauce, then bring to the boil.

Once boiling, remove from the heat and stir in the soy milk. Transfer the contents of the pan to a casserole dish, placing the potato slices in layers. Sprinkle the parsley over the top (if using), then layer the tomato slices on top and sprinkle with the cheese (if using).

Cover with aluminium foil and bake in the oven for 90 minutes. Serve hot.

SERVES 4–6

BAKED SOYBEANS IN EGGPLANT

Cal : 404   kJ : 1688   Chol : 48 mg   Ca : 271 mg

1 large eggplant (aubergine), about 300–350 g (10–11 oz)
1 teaspoon soybean oil
1 small onion, diced
1 clove garlic, diced
50 g (2 oz) minced (ground) beef or lamb
4 tablespoons soybeans in tomato sauce (see page 63)
1 small tomato, about 60 g (2 oz), diced
60 g (2 oz) cauliflower, cut into small florets
salt and freshly ground black pepper, to taste
3 or 4 sweet basil leaves, shredded
2 tablespoons grated cheese

Preheat the oven to 160°C (325°F).

Cut the eggplant lengthwise and carve out the inside of the eggplant to form the shape of a boat. Reserve the flesh for another use, such as a vegetable curry.

Heat the soybean oil in a saucepan over a medium heat and sauté the onion and garlic until brown. Add the beef, soybeans, tomato and cauliflower. Season to taste with salt and pepper. Cook for 2 minutes.

Place the eggplant skin side down in an ovenproof dish or casserole. Pack the meat filling into the dug out eggplant. Sprinkle the basil and cheese over the top. Bake in the oven for 40 minutes.

Serve hot with boiled noodles and green salad.

SERVES 2

Soybeans in tomato sauce are available in cans, marketed by Sanitarium and plain by Masterfoods, among others.
You can use home-cooked soybeans in tomato sauce. The recipe is found on page 63. However, reduce the amount of tomatoes if using home-cooked soybeans in tomato sauce.
Eggplants stuffed with Soybean Vindaloo (page 78) is tasty variation of this recipe.

STIR-FRIED TEMPEH
AND VEGETABLES

Cal : 528   kJ : 2219   Chol : 0 mg   Ca : 358 mg

100 g (3^1/$_2$ oz) tempeh
2 teaspoons cornflour (cornstarch)
2 cloves garlic, diced
2 teaspoons soybean oil
1 medium carrot, cut into rings or julienne
100 g (3^1/$_2$ oz) baby corn (spears), halved lengthwise
60 g (2 oz) broccoli, cut into small florets
120 g (4 oz) sugar snap peas, ends trimmed
2 tablespoons oyster sauce
1 tablespoon light soy sauce
^{1}/$_4$ teaspoon salt
freshly ground black pepper, to taste
^{1}/$_2$ medium red capsicum (sweet pepper), cut into chunks
^{1}/$_3$ cup (90 mL, 3 fl oz) water

Cut the tempeh into slices ^{1}/$_2$ cm (^{1}/$_4$ in) thick, then cut each slice into three pieces. Sprinkle over 1^1/$_2$ teaspoons of the cornflour to coat the tempeh pieces.

Sauté half of the garlic in 1 teaspoon of the soybean oil. Add the tempeh and sauté until brown on the surface, about 5–6 minutes. Add the carrot and stir-fry for 2 minutes before adding the baby corn.

Cook for 2 minutes, then add the broccoli, sugar snap peas, oyster sauce, soy sauce, salt and pepper to taste. Stir for a minute before adding the capsicum. Sprinkle in some of the water if too dry.

Mix the remaining ^{1}/$_2$ teaspoon cornflour with the remaining water and add to the vegetables. Stir well and cover for a minute before transferring to a serving plate or dish.

Serve with steamed rice, noodles or quiche.

SERVES 3–4

TOFU IN OYSTER SAUCE

Cal : 602   kJ : 2528   Chol : 0 mg   Ca : 220 mg

300 g (10 oz) silken tofu
2 tablespoons soybean oil
1 clove garlic, diced
1 small red onion, diced
2 tablespoons oyster sauce
1 tablespoon light soy sauce
1/4 cup (60 mL, 2 fl oz) liquid stock
freshly ground black pepper, to taste
1/2 teaspoon cornflour (cornstarch)
fresh coriander or celery leaves, to garnish

Cut the tofu into six pieces.

Heat the soybean oil in a wok and stir-fry the garlic and onion until fragrant. Remove from the wok and set aside.

Now gently stir-fry the tofu, as it breaks up very easily. When golden brown in colour, transfer the tofu onto a serving dish.

Reduce the heat to very low. Return the garlic and onion to the wok, and add the oyster sauce, light soy sauce, liquid stock, pepper to taste and cornflour, stirring all the time.

Bring to the boil, then pour the sauce over the cooked tofu. Garnish with fresh coriander or celery leaves.

Serve hot accompanied by steamed rice and stir-fried vegetable dishes.

SERVES 3–4

Oyster sauce is readily available from most supermarkets and Asian food stores. The sauce is made from extracts of oyster, caramel and other additives. The different brands do vary in content: some contain MSG and preservatives, while others are preservative-free. Check the label before making your purchase.

SPICY CHICKPEAS

Cal : 743   kJ : 3133   Chol : 0 mg   Ca : 326 mg

200 g (7 oz) chickpeas (garbanzo beans)
1³/₄ cups (400 mL, 14 fl oz) plus 1 tablespoon water
1 tablespoon oil
¹/₂ medium onion, diced
1 teaspoon garam masala
1 teaspoon cumin seeds
¹/₂ teaspoon chilli powder
2 tablespoons chopped fresh stalks of coriander (Chinese parsley)
1 teaspoon salt
2 tomatoes, about 300 g (10 oz), roughly chopped
fresh coriander (Chinese parsley) leaves, to garnish

Soak the chickpeas overnight and discard any bad peas.

Cook the chickpeas in a pressure cooker with 1³/₄ cups (400 mL, 14 fl oz) water. Continue cooking for 10 minutes after it has pressurised. Drain and reserve the stock for later use. Alternatively, boil in an ordinary saucepan for 1 hour until soft.

Heat the oil in a saucepan or wok over a low heat, and sauté the onion until it is translucent.

Make a paste of the garam masala, cumin seeds and chilli powder with the 1 tablespoon water. Add the paste to the onions and sauté until fragrant.

Add the coriander stalks, chickpeas and salt. Stir through, then add the tomatoes. Add 1¹/₄ cups (300 mL, 10 fl oz) of the reserved cooking stock and simmer for 30–40 minutes, or until the sauce has reduced by two-thirds.

Serve hot garnished with fresh coriander leaves.

SERVES 4–6

Note: This recipe is adapted from one provided by Dr A. Gulati.

Chickpeas contain second-class proteins and phytoestrogens. They are conveniently available cooked in cans, as well as in dried form.

STEAMED FISH WITH TOFU

Cal : 622   kJ : 2612   Chol : 140 mg   Ca : 284 mg

200 g (7 oz) firm, white fish fillet, such as ling
1 tablespoon oyster sauce
1 tablespoon soy sauce
1 teaspoon white wine
12 slices fresh ginger
1 tablespoon cornflour (cornstarch)
3 teaspoons soybean oil
1 clove garlic, diced
300 g (10 oz) silken firm tofu
spring onion or coriander (Chinese parsley) leaves, to garnish

Cut the fish fillet lengthwise into pieces 1 cm ($1/2$ in) thick.

Place in a suitable dish with the oyster sauce, soy sauce, wine, ginger and cornflour. Marinate in the refrigerator for 20–30 minutes.

Heat the soybean oil in saucepan and sauté the garlic until light brown. Set aside to cool.

Cut the tofu into sheets 1 cm ($1/2$ in) thick. Brush a heatproof ceramic dish lightly with the cooled garlic oil, and layer the tofu over the bottom of the dish.

Place portions of the fish fillet on top of each piece of tofu. Brush the top of the fish with some more of the garlic oil and place a slice of ginger on top of each portion.

Place the dish in a steamer or large saucepan on a rack. Steam for 10 minutes.

Garnish with spring onion or coriander leaves, and serve hot with steamed rice.

SERVES 3–4

Ling fish fillet is readily available and has very little bone on the fillet. Other fish fillets can be used instead, provided that all bones are removed before cooking.
Whole fish such as bream, snapper, barramundi and coral trout can be steamed with tofu, but score the sides of the fish before marinating. Make sure your tofu is fresh, otherwise the dish will turn sourish in taste.

SWEET AND SOUR TOFU

Cal : 718   kJ : 3016   Chol : 0 mg   Ca : 234 mg

300 g (10 oz) silken firm tofu
2 tablespoons soybean oil
$^1/_2$ medium carrot, cut into julienne
2 tablespoons apple cider vinegar
1 medium onion, sliced
$^1/_2$ teaspoon salt
2 tablespoons tomato sauce (ketchup)
100 g (3$^1/_2$ oz) cucumber, cut into chunks
$^1/_2$ cup (70 g, 2$^1/_2$ oz) pineapple pieces, cut into chunks
$^1/_2$ medium red capsicum (sweet pepper), cut into chunks
1 tablespoon sugar
freshly ground black pepper, to taste
$^1/_2$ teaspoon cornflour (cornstarch)
1 $^1/_2$ tablespoons water

Cut the tofu into 2 cm ($^3/_4$ in) cubes. Heat 1 tablespoon of the soybean oil in a wok and fry the tofu cubes until they are golden brown on all sides.

Marinate the carrot in the apple cider vinegar.

Cut the onions into strips by sectioning each into eight wedges and separating into pieces. Sauté the onion in the remaining 1 tablespoon soybean oil for 2 minutes, then add the carrot and the apple cider vinegar in which it was marinated.

Add the salt, tomato sauce, cucumber, pineapple and capsicum. Stir well before adding the sugar and pepper to taste. Mix the cornflour with the water, then add to the vegetable mixture. Stir through well.

Bring to the boil and add the tofu. Stir thoroughly before serving hot with steamed rice.

SERVES 2–4

Note: Tempeh can be used instead of tofu in this recipe. Tempeh is rather salty and stronger in flavour than tofu. Use only 150 g (5 oz) in the above recipe. Cut into smaller cubes and fry until brown before adding to the sweet and sour mixture. Serve with steamed rice.

STIR-FRIED FRENCH BEANS WITH PINE NUTS

Cal : 584   kJ : 2408   Chol : 0 mg   Ca : 227 mg

500 g (1 lb) fresh French (runner or string) beans
1 tablespoon soybean oil
2 tablespoons pine nuts
1 clove garlic, finely diced
1 tablespoon light soy sauce
1 tablespoon oyster sauce
$1/4$ cup (60 mL, 2 fl oz) water or stock
$1/2$ teaspoon cornflour (cornstarch)
pinch of ground black pepper (optional)

Rinse the beans and remove ends, before cutting each bean into 2–4 cm ($3/4$–$1 1/2$ in) lengths. Drain well.

Add 2 drops of the soybean oil to a wok over a medium heat. Roast the pine nuts for 5 minutes, taking care not to scorch. Remove the pine nuts from the wok and spread out on absorbent kitchen paper to cool.

Heat the remaining soybean oil in the wok over high heat. Sauté the garlic until brown, then add the beans and stir-fry for a couple of minutes before adding the light soy sauce and oyster sauce. Cover for 1 minute, then stir well.

Mix the cornflour with the water, then add to the wok. Cook for a further 5 minutes.

Stir in the pine nuts and serve immediately.

SERVES 3–4

Note: This dish goes well with steamed rice, pasta, noodles or meat.

Fresh beans contains coumestrol and lignans.
The concentration of coumestrol in fresh French beans is about the same as a similar weight of dried soybeans. However, it is 60 to 70 times less than that present in soybean sprouts.
The seedling of the French bean is reported to contain estradiol, a natural estrogen found in the blood of the human female.

STIR-FRIED TOFU CUTLET WITH VEGETABLES

Cal : 335   kJ : 1406   Chol : 69 mg   Ca : 251 mg

100 g (3 $^1/_2$ oz) chicken fillet
1 tablespoon soy sauce
1 tablespoon oyster sauce
1 teaspoon cornflour (cornstarch)
2 slices fresh ginger, finely diced
1 tablespoon canola or soybean oil
2 cloves garlic, diced
150 g (5 oz) cauliflower, cut into small florets
scant $^1/_2$ cup (100 mL, 3$^1/_2$ fl oz) water
$^1/_2$ teaspoon salt
100 g (3$^1/_2$ oz) tofu cutlet, cut into slices
100 g (3$^1/_2$ oz) broccoli, cut into small florets
1 small can champignons, drained and rinsed (125 g, 4 oz)

Remove any visible fat from the chicken and discard. Cut the chicken into strips. Marinate the chicken in the soy sauce, oyster sauce, $^1/_2$ teaspoon of the cornflour and ginger.

Heat the oil in a wok or frying pan. When nearly smoking, add the garlic and sauté until fragrant.

Add the chicken and its marinade. Stir-fry for 3 minutes before adding the cauliflower. Stir through well, then add 1$^1/_2$ tablespoons of the water. Season with the salt, stir through, then cover the wok and allow to cook for 2 minutes.

Add the tofu, broccoli and champignons. Stir through well and cook for a further 4–5 minutes. Add more water if necessary.

Use the remaining water to make a paste with the cornflour. Add to the wok to thicken the sauce slightly. Stir-fry for a further 2 minutes.

Serve hot with rice.

SERVES 4

SPRING ROLLS

Cal : 1244   kJ : 5225   Chol : 98 mg   Ca : 297 mg

200 g (7 oz) minced (ground) pork
1 tablespoon light soy sauce
1 tablespoon oyster sauce
150 g (5 oz) bean shoots or sprouts
100 g (3$^1/_2$ oz) bamboo shoots
10 stalks of garlic chives
400 g (14 oz) cabbage, shredded
150 g (5 oz) diced carrot
soybean oil
1 clove garlic, diced
1 teaspoon salt
small pinch of ground black pepper
1 tablespoon cornflour (cornstarch)
scant $^1/_3$ cup (80 mL, 2$^3/_4$ fl oz) water
1 x medium packet spring roll wrappers, 20 x 20 cm (8 x 8 in) sheets

Marinate the pork in the light soy sauce and oyster sauce.

Rinse the bean shoots and cut the bamboo shoots into strips similar in size to the bean shoots. Cut the chives into similar lengths. Drain well and pat dry with absorbent kitchen paper.

Heat 2 teaspoons soybean oil in a wok over a medium heat. Sauté the garlic in the oil until fragrant, then add the pork and its marinade. Stir-fry for 3 minutes. Increase the heat to high before adding the cabbage, bamboo shoots and carrots. Stir-fry for 2 minutes, then add the bean shoots, salt, pepper and chives. Stir through well before transferring to a metal colander to cool and drain off sauces.

Mix the cornflour with the water to make a paste, and cook in the microwave on high for 45 seconds.

Divide the filling into 20 portions and wrap in the spring roll wrappers, tucking in the ends of the wrapper as you roll. Seal the edges with the cornflour paste. Deep-fry in soybean oil until medium brown, then drain on absorbent kitchen paper. (Alternatively, bake in a preheated 160°C (325°F) oven for 30 minutes, after brushing the wrappers with egg white.)

Serve hot with tomato ketchup or sweet and sour sauce.

SERVES 6–10

PICKLED CURRIED VEGETABLES

Cal : 1743   kJ : 7415   Chol : 0 mg   Ca : 485 mg

400 g (14 oz) cucumber
3 long red chilli peppers
200 g (7 oz) carrots
100 g (3 $^{1}/_{2}$ oz) green or French (string) beans
400 g (14 oz) cabbage
400 g (14 oz) cauliflower
2 tablespoons sesame seeds
8 cloves garlic
1 medium onion
2 tablespoons curry powder
$^{1}/_{4}$ cup (60 mL, 2 fl oz) water
5 tablespoons soybean oil
$^{3}/_{4}$ cup (185 mlL, 6 fl oz) apple cider vinegar
2 tablespoons sugar
2 tablespoons salt
$^{1}/_{4}$ teaspoon monosodium glutamate (MSG)
$^{1}/_{4}$ cup (50 g, 1$^{3}/_{4}$ oz) crushed roasted peanuts

Rinse all the vegetables and cut the cucumber, chilli peppers and carrots into strips. Slice the beans into 4 cm (1$^{3}/_{4}$ in) lengths and the cabbage into 2 x 5 cm ($^{3}/_{4}$ x 2 in) pieces. Cut the cauliflower into florets.

Spread all the vegetables out on baking trays or sheets. Stand out in the sun for at least 4 hours to semi-dry the vegetables.

Lightly toast the sesame seeds in a frying pan or skillet, and set aside. Bruise the garlic and cut into quarters. Dice the onion very finely. Make the curry powder into a paste with the water.

Heat the soybean oil in a hot wok. Sauté the onion for a minute, then add the curry paste and reduce the heat to medium. Sauté until the mixture is very fragrant before adding the vinegar, sugar, salt and monosodium glutamate.

Increase the heat to high once more, and add the carrots, cabbage and cauliflower. Mix well before adding the beans and garlic. Make sure the sauce is boiling before adding the chilli pepper and cucumber. Stir quickly and, when the sauce has returned to the boil, transfer to a shallow dish and allow to cool.

Sprinkle the peanuts and sesame seeds over the top. Serve cold with rice and satay or teriyaki chicken.

SERVES 8–12

Note: The best results are achieved when this dish is cooked a day or two ahead of time. It will keep for up to a week in the refrigerator.

TOFU CUTLET IN LETTUCE LEAVES

Cal : 874   kJ : 3670   Chol : 247 mg   Ca : 358 mg

100 g (3^1/$_2$ oz) fresh banana prawns (shrimp), peeled and deveined
1 teaspoon light soy sauce
200 g (7 oz) minced (ground) pork
1 tablespoon dark soy sauce
1 teaspoon oyster sauce
20 g (3/4 oz) dried Chinese or shiitake mushrooms
1 medium onion
100 g (3^1/$_2$ oz) water chestnuts
100 g (3^1/$_2$ oz) tofu cutlet
12 lettuce leaves
2 tablespoons soybean oil
1 teaspoon cornflour (cornstarch)
scant ^{1}/$_4$ cup (60 mL, 2 fl oz) water or stock
^{1}/$_4$ teaspoon salt
2 pinches of ground black pepper

Cut the prawns into ^{1}/$_2$ cm (^{1}/$_4$ in) cubes, then marinate in the light soy sauce.

Marinate the pork in the dark soy sauce and oyster sauce.

Soak the mushrooms in hot water and clean off the dirt before cutting in small dice. Dice the onions and water chestnuts, and cut the tofu into ^{1}/$_2$ cm (^{1}/$_4$ in) cubes. Rinse the lettuce leaves and trim to make a round shape. Drain well.

Heat the soybean oil in a wok. Sauté the onions for 2 minutes before adding the pork and mushrooms. Stir-fry for 5 minutes, then add the water chestnuts and tofu.

Mix the cornflour with the water, salt and pepper. Add to the wok

109

and stir through, then add the prawns and continue stirring until the prawns are cooked, about 3–4 minutes.

When the mixture is nearly dry, spoon some of the mixture into each of the individual lettuce leaf rounds. Serve immediately.
SERVES 4–6

Note: This dish can be served as an entree or appetiser, or as part of the main course with steamed rice and salads. Omit prawns if allergic to seafood or unavailable.

STIR-FRIED SNOW PEAS
AND TOFU

Cal :1642   kJ : 6900   Chol : 378 mg   Ca : 784 mg

200 g (7 oz) fresh prawns (shrimp), peeled and deveined
2 tablespoons soy sauce
2 tablespoons oyster sauce
1 teaspoon white wine
300 g (10 oz) firm tofu
3 tablespoons cornflour (cornstarch)
5 tablespoons cooking oil
200 g (7 oz) snow peas (mangetout), rinsed and ends trimmed
$1/2$ teaspoon salt
$1/2$ teaspoon sugar
$1/4$ cup (60 mL, 2 fl oz) plus 1 tablespoon chicken stock
1 medium onion, peeled and cut into 1 cm ($1/2$ in) strips

Marinate the prawns in the soy sauce, 1 tablespoon of the oyster sauce
and the wine for 10 minutes.

Remove the tofu from its package gently and cut into 3–4 cm
($1^1/4$–$1^3/4$ in) cubes. Pat dry with absorbent kitchen paper.

Heat 3 tablespoons of the cooking oil in a nonstick saucepan and
coat the tofu in 2 tablespoons of the cornflour. When the oil in the pan is
smoking, fry the tofu until it is brown on all sides. Remove from the pan,
drain off excess oil and arrange on a serving plate.

In a clean wok or saucepan, heat the remaining 2 tablespoons of
cooking oil over a medium heat. Stir-fry the marinated prawns for
3 minutes, then remove from the wok. Now add the snow peas and
onion, and stir-fry together for 4 minutes.

Add the $1/4$ cup (60 mL, 2 fl oz) stock, the remaining 1 tablespoon
oyster sauce and 1 tablespoon soy sauce, and the sugar and salt.

Return the prawns to the wok. Mix the remaining 1 tablespoon
cornflour with the 1 tablespoon stock, and add to the prawn mixture to
thicken the sauce. Cook for a further 2 minutes.

Pour the prawn mixture and its sauce on top of the cooked tofu.
Serve with rice or instant noodles.

SERVES 4

111

SOY CURRY PUFFS

Cal : 2347   kJ : 9715   Chol : 407 mg   Ca : 478 mg

200 g (7 oz) minced (ground) beef
1 tablespoon light soy sauce
$1/_4$ teaspoon sugar
1 teaspoon curry powder
$1/_2$ cube beef stock
200 g (7 oz) potatoes
scant $1/_3$ cup (80 mL, $2^3/_4$ fl oz) soybean oil
1 small onion, diced
$3/_4$ cup (100 g, $3^1/_2$ oz) frozen green or garden peas, rinsed and drained
$1^1/_3$ cups (160 g, $5^1/_2$ oz) self-raising flour
$2/_3$ cup (50 g, $1^3/_4$ oz) soy flour
pinch of salt
1 large egg, beaten
$1^1/_2$ tablespoons cold water
egg white, to seal pastry

Preheat the oven to 160°C (325°F).

Marinate the beef in the soy sauce, sugar, curry powder and stock cube.

Boil potatoes in water for 5 minutes, then peel and cut into $1/_2$ cm ($1/_4$ in) cubes.

Heat 2 teaspoons of the soybean oil in a frying pan or skillet over a medium heat. Add the onion and sauté until fragrant and starting to brown. Add the marinated beef and sauté for a further 3 minutes.

Now add the peas and potatoes. Cook for 3 minutes, adding a little water if necessary to keep the filling moist, but not too wet. Set aside to cool.

Sift the self-raising flour and soy flour together into a stainless steel bowl. Add the salt and mix in the remaining soybean oil. Add the beaten egg and work into a dough, if necessary adding just enough of the cold water to make the pastry soft and pliable.

Roll out half of the pastry on a floured surface and cut into round shapes with a round pastry cutter, or use a small rice bowl if you do not have a cutter large enough.

Divide the beef filling between each round of pastry and place some filling in the centre of each one. Fold the pastry in half over the filling, sealing the edges with egg white and fluting the edges by pinching the pastry between your fingers. Brush the top of the pastry with a little soy milk.

Place the curry puffs on a baking sheet (or two if necessary) and bake in the oven for 30 minutes, or until golden brown.
MAKES 12–15

SOYARONI SALMON CASSEROLE

Using block cheese
Cal : 2394   kJ : 10 054   Chol : 351 mg   Ca : 2307 mg
Using soy cheese
Cal : 2354 kJ : 9914 Chol : 185 mg Ca : 1887 mg

200 g (7 oz) soyaroni pasta
1 tablespoon soybean oil
2 medium onions
1 x 210 g (7 oz) can red salmon, drained
300 g (10 oz) silken tofu
350 mL (11 1/2 fl oz) water
1/2 teaspoon salt
1/8 teaspoon ground black pepper
1 teaspoon French onion stock powder
1 tablespoon cornflour (cornstarch)
2 medium tomatoes, about 125 (4 oz) each, sliced
1 3/4 cups (200 g, 7 oz) grated cheddar cheese or soy cheese

Preheat the oven to 180°C (350°F). Cook the soyaroni pasta in a large saucepan of boiling water for 12 minutes. Drain well.

Heat the soybean oil in a large saucepan. Dice 1 onion and add to the pan. Sauté until fragrant, then add the salmon.

Blend the tofu in 2/3 cup (150 mL, 5 fl oz) of the water. Add the tofu, salt, pepper and French onion stock to the salmon mixture. Add 2/3 cup (150 mL, 5 fl oz) more of the water.

Mix the cornflour with the remaining scant 1/4 cup (50 mL,

$1^1/_2$ fl oz) water and stir into the salmon mixture to thicken the sauce.

Add the soyaroni pasta and stir through. Cut the remaining onion into slices and line a casserole dish with the slices. Pour half of the pasta mixture into the dish, spreading out slightly to cover the bottom of the dish. Place the tomatoes in a layer on top of this, then cover with the remaining pasta mixture. Sprinke the cheese over the top.

Cover the dish with aluminium foil and bake in the oven for 20 minutes. Serve hot, accompanied by a garden salad.

SERVES 4–6

> Soy milk can be used instead of tofu in this dish. Reduce the amount of water to a scant $1/_4$ cup (50 mL, $1^1/_2$ fl oz) and use $1^3/_4$ cups (400 mL, 14 fl oz) soy milk.

SOYARONI SALAD

Cal : 1244   kJ : 5152   Chol : 49 mg   Ca : 200 mg

200 g (7 oz) soyaroni pasta
1 cup (150 g, 5 oz) frozen green or garden peas
20 g ($3/_4$ oz) ham, diced
$1/_2$ tablespoon diced onion
$1/_4$ level cup (40 g, $1^1/_2$ oz) shredded carrot
$1/_4$ teaspoon salt
$1/_4$ teaspoon sugar
freshly ground black pepper, to taste
6 tablespoons mayonnaise (use tofu mayonnaise if time permits — see recipe on page 49)
1 tablespoon grated cheese (optional)

Cook the soyaroni pasta in 6 cups (1.5 litres, $2^1/_2$ imp. pints) of boiling salted water for 12 minutes. Cool quickly in cold water and drain well.

Cook the peas in boiling water for 4–5 minutes. Cool quickly in cold water and drain well. Combine all the ingredients except the cheese and refrigerate for at least 1 hour before serving.

Add your favourite shredded cheese if you fancy a cheesy flavour and serve cold with cold or barbecued meats. A green salad complements this dish very nicely.

SERVES 4–6

TOFU WITH MINCED MEAT

Cal : 493   kJ : 2071   Chol : 63 mg   Ca : 221 mg

100 g (3¹/₂ oz) minced (ground) meat, such as pork, beef or lamb
1 tablespoon light soy sauce
1 tablespoon oyster sauce
1 teaspoon white wine
2 tablespoons cornflour (cornstarch)
freshly ground black pepper, to taste
1 teaspoon soybean oil
1 clove garlic, finely diced
300 g (10 oz) silken tofu, cut into 1 cm (¹/₂ in) cubes
1 tablespoon dark soy sauce
¹/₄ cup (60 mL, 2 fl oz) water
¹/₄ teaspoon sugar
pinch of salt
fresh coriander (Chinese parsley) leaves or spring onion stems, to garnish

Marinate the meat with the light soy sauce, oyster sauce, wine,
1 tablespoon of the cornflour and pepper to taste.

Heat the soybean oil in a wok or frying pan until nearly smoking.
Add the garlic and sauté until fragrant, then add the meat and its
marinade. Cook the meat for 4–5 minutes over a high heat.

Add the tofu and dark soy sauce. Cover the wok and allow to
cook for 2–3 minutes.

Mix the remaining 1 tablespoon cornflour and the water into a
paste and add to the wok. Bring to the boil to allow the sauce to thicken.

Check the seasoning and add the sugar and salt if necessary.

Garnish with fresh coriander or spring onion stems, and serve hot
with boiled rice.

SERVES 2–4

This is a popular Cantonese dish which is easy to prepare and
cook. Minced pork is normally used, but beef and chicken fillets
can be substituted here, resulting in different flavours.
An accompanying dish such as steamed vegetables or a stir-fried
combination is most suitable.

BEAN SHOOTS IN FISH SAUCE

Cal : 342   kJ : 1413   Chol : 0 mg   Ca : 53 mg

250 g (8 oz) bean shoots or sprouts
1 tablespoon soybean oil
2 cloves garlic, diced
1 tablespoon light soy sauce
2 tablespoons fish sauce
1 tablespoon sesame seeds, lightly toasted
1 small red capsicum (sweet pepper), seeded and shredded, to garnish
fresh coriander (Chinese parsley) leaves, to garnish

Bring 4 cups (1 litre, 1³/₄ imp. pints) water to the boil in a medium saucepan.

Blanch the bean shoots in the boiling water for 30 seconds. Drain well in a colander.

Discard the water and heat the soybean oil in the saucepan. Add the garlic and sauté until light brown and fragrant.

Add the light soy sauce and fish sauce. Stir in the blanched bean shoots and mix quickly before transferring to a serving dish.

Sprinkle the sesame seeds over the top of the bean shoots. Garnish with capsicum and coriander leaves, and serve hot with rice.
SERVES 2–4

Fresh bean shoots cook very quickly and do not stand reheating at all.
They are readily available everywhere and also very cheap.
Fresh bean shoots are sprouted from mung beans and are quite easy to grow at home.
Bean shoots are very rich in vitamin C, B group vitamins and protein, although it is only a second-class protein.
The phytoestrogens present are mainly in the form of lignans and coumestrol.

STICKY RICE PUDDING

Cal : 1401   kJ : 5733   Chol : 8 mg   Ca : 260 mg

1 cup (160 g, 5 oz) black glutinous rice
1 cup (190 g, 6 $1/2$ oz) white glutinous rice
$2^1/2$ cups (625 mL, 1 imp. pint) boiling water
4 tablespoons coconut powder
5 tablespoons soft brown sugar
1 x 75 g ($2^1/2$ oz) packet egg custard mix
2 cups (500 mL, 16 fl oz) fat-reduced soy milk

Soak both rices together in a bowl of cold water overnight. Pick out any debris and unmilled rice grains, then drain.

Transfer the rice to a large (at least 10–12 cup or 2.5–3 litre, 4–4$3/4$ imp. pint capacity) ceramic microwave-proof dish with a lid. Add the coconut powder and boiling water. Cook in the microwave oven on high for 10 minutes with the lid on.

Stir the rice and microwave on medium for a further 4 minutes, then mix in the brown sugar and cook for a further 4 minutes on medium.

Pack the rice in a serving bowl or lasagne dish. Compress the rice with a wooden spoon and set aside.

Combine the egg custard mix and the soy milk, and cook, stirring, until starting to thicken.

Strain the custard if necessary. Pour over the top of the rice and allow to cool before placing in the refrigerator.

Serve cold or warm as desired. If using a lasagne dish, slice into diamond shapes before removing from the dish into individual dessert plates. Pour the Coconut Sauce over the top (see recipe on page 118) and serve.

SERVES 6–8

> Black glutinous rice is moderately sticky, while white glutinous rice is very sticky, hence the common name of sticky rice. Both types of rice are used frequently in Eastern desserts. Some supermarkets may stock them, but you should have no trouble finding them in Asian food stores or oriental markets.

COCONUT SAUCE

Cal : 296   kJ : 1212   Chol : 0 mg   Ca : 8 mg

6 tablespoons coconut powder
$^2/_3$ cup (150 mL, 5 fl oz) hot water
1 tablespoon sugar
1 tablespoon cornflour (cornstarch)
$1^1/_2$ tablespoons cold water

Dissolve the coconut powder in the hot water in a saucepan, then add the sugar. Stir to dissolve.

Make a paste out of the cornflour and cold water. Stir into the coconut mixture and bring to the boil. Strain the sauce if necessary.

Pour 1–1$^1/_2$ tablespoons on top of each serving of Sticky Rice Pudding.

RED BEAN AND BLACK RICE DESSERT

Cal : 1353   kJ : 5562   Chol : 0 mg   Ca : 200 mg

1 cup (200 g, 7 oz) adzuki (red) beans
$^1/_2$ cup (90 g, 3 oz) black glutinous rice, rinsed
8 cups (2 litres, 3$^1/_4$ imp. pints) water
8 level tablespoons sugar
coconut cream or powder (optional)

Wash the red beans and discard any debris. Soak for 1 hour in hot water.

Place the beans in a deep saucepan and add the black rice. Pour over the water and bring to the boil and simmer for 2 hours.

Add the sugar to taste, then cook for a further 30 minutes.

Serve warm in soup bowls with a swirl of coconut cream or dusting of coconut powder (if using).

SERVES 6–8

CHERRY MUFFINS

Cal : 2274   kJ : 9364   Chol : 525 mg   Ca : 665 mg

$^3/_4$ cup (125 g, 4 oz) soft brown sugar
1 tablespoon honey
$^1/_4$ cup (60 mL, 2 fl oz) plus 1 tablespoon canola oil
2 large eggs, beaten
$^1/_2$ cup (40 g, 1$^1/_2$ oz) soy flour
1 cup (125 g, 4 oz) wholemeal self-raising flour
$^1/_2$ teaspoon baking powder
$^2/_3$ cup (150 mL, 5 fl oz) soy milk
1 cup (200 g, 7 oz) pitted cherries, halved

Preheat the oven to 180°C (350°F). Lightly grease muffin pans.

Mix the brown sugar, honey and oil together in a large mixing bowl. Add the eggs to mixture and combine thoroughly.

Sift in the soy flour, wholemeal flour and baking powder, and fold through well.

Add the soy milk and stir until the batter is smooth. Fold in the cherries.

Spoon the batter into the prepared muffin pans and bake in the oven for about 20 minutes. Test with a wooden skewer after 17 minutes to check if cooked. When the skewer comes out clean, remove from the oven.

Allow the muffins to cool in the pan on a wire rack for a few minutes before turning out. They will keep for a few days if stored in an airtight container.

MAKES 10–12 LARGE MUFFINS OR 28–30 SMALL MUFFINS

Canned pitted cherries can be used in this recipe.
Cherries contain phytoestrogens.
The batter may smell a little queer when wet because of the soy flour, but the smell invariably disappears with cooking.
The eggs in this recipe can be substituted with an extra 1 tablespoon soy milk for each egg or egg scrambler.

SOY AND OATMEAL COOKIES

Cal : 2745   kJ : 11 304   Chol : 481 mg   Ca : 483 mg

100 g (3 $^1/_2$ oz) butter, softened
$^3/_4$ cup (125 g, 4 oz) soft brown sugar
1 large egg
2 teaspoons vanilla essence (extract)
scant $^1/_2$ cup (100 mL, 3$^1/_2$ fl oz) low-fat soy milk
$^1/_2$ cup (40 g, 1$^1/_2$ oz) soy flour
$^1/_2$ cup (60 g, 2 oz) plain (all-purpose) flour
$^1/_2$ teaspoon bicarbonate of soda
2 teaspoons ground cinnamon
2.5 cups (225 g, 7 oz) quick-cooking rolled oats
1 teaspoon soybean oil, for oiling hands

Preheat the oven to 160°C (325°F). Grease two baking sheets.

Cream the butter and brown sugar together well. Beat in the egg and vanilla, and then the soy milk. Combine thoroughly.

Sift the soy flour, plain flour, bicarbonate of soda and cinnamon together. Add to the creamed mixture and mix well. Now add the rolled oats and mix until the dough is thoroughly combined.

Place a tablespoon of the dough into your oiled hands. Roll into a round ball before pressing the dough flat with the palms of your hands. Place the cookies on the baking sheets and bake in the oven for 20 minutes. Remove from the oven and slide the cookies off the baking sheets and onto a wire rack to cool.

MAKES ABOUT 28 COOKIES

Note: Five of these cookies contain approximately the same amount of phytoestrogens as 100 mL (3$^1/_2$ fl oz) of high-protein soy milk.

Soy flour keeps better if stored in an airtight container in the refrigerator. Soy flour is heavier than wheat flour and retains a lot of moisture after baking. Rolled oats are very rich in fibre and also contain phytoestrogens.

SOY CARROT CAKE

Cal : 3076   kJ : 12643   Chol : 525 mg   Ca : 327 mg

$^1/_2$ cup (40 g, 1$^1/_2$ oz) soy flour
$^1/_2$ cup (60 g, 2 oz) self-raising flour
1 teaspoon baking powder
$^1/_2$ teaspoon bicarbonate of soda
1$^1/_2$ teaspoons ground cinnamon
$^1/_2$ teaspoon salt
$^2/_3$ cup (150 mL, 5 fl oz) soybean or canola oil
2 eggs
$^3/_4$ cup (185 g, 6 oz) sugar
$^1/_2$ cup (10 g, 3$^1/_2$ oz) pineapple pieces, chopped into smaller chunks
1 cup (185 g, 6 oz) shredded carrots
$^1/_4$ cup (30 g, 1 oz) chopped pecans

Preheat the oven to 180°C (350°F). Grease a 25 cm (10 in) round or 22 cm (9 in) square cake pan.

Sift the soy flour, self-raising flour, baking powder, bicarbonate of soda, cinnamon and salt together into a bowl.

Beat the oil, sugar and eggs together in a separate bowl. Gradually add the sifted dry ingredients, stirring continuously, until everything is well incorporated.

Add the pineapple, carrots and pecan nuts and stir into the batter. Pour the batter into the prepared cake pan.

Bake in the oven for 50–60 minutes, or until a skewer inserted into the centre of the cake comes out clean.

Allow to cool slightly in the pan before turning out onto a wire rack to cool. Store in an airtight container. This cake also freezes very well.

SERVES 6–8

121

CREAM CHEESE FROSTING

If you want to frost this cake, beat together 60 g (2 oz) butter, $1/2$ teaspoon vanilla essence (extract) and 125 g (4 oz) cream cheese. Slowly add $1^1/2$ cups (250 g, 8 oz) icing (confectioners') sugar to the creamed mixture, beating continuously, until you reach the desired consistency.

Note: This recipe is adapted from a carrot cake recipe provided by Mrs Sherry Jordan.

Frosting is very sweet and high in calories, so simply leave the cake unfrosted if you are on a weight reduction program. The cream cheese frosting is not suitable for freezing.

SOY PIKELETS OR PANCAKES

Cal : 1098   kJ : 4517   Chol : 225 mg   Ca : 457 mg

$1/2$ cup (40 g, $1^1/2$ oz) soy flour
1 cup (125 g, 4 oz) self-raising flour
pinch of salt
$1/4$ teaspoon baking powder
1 large egg, beaten
2 tablespoons sugar
scant 1 cup (200 mL, 7 fl oz) soy milk
1 tablespoon soybean oil, for cooking

Sift the soy flour, flour, salt and baking powder twice. Make a well in the centre of the dry ingredients and add the egg. Mix together with a spoon, gradually drawing in more of the flour from the sides as you go.

Now add the sugar and milk, and mix until the batter is smooth.

Heat a frying pan or crêpe pan over a medium to hight heat. Grease with the soybean oil. When hot, drop 2 tablespoonsful of batter for each pikelet into the pan. Gently level out the batter into a round shape using the back of a spoon.

When the pikelets are golden brown underneath, turn them over and cook on the other side. Adjust the heat while cooking if necessary.

Serve with your favourite jam and freshly whipped cream.

SERVES 4–6

SOY CURD DESSERT IN VANILLA SYRUP

Cal : 548   kJ : 2302   Chol : 0 mg   Ca : 1 mg

1 x 65 g (2 oz) packet tofu mix
(contains 1 bag soy powder and 1 bag glucono delta lactone)
3¼ cups (800 mL, 26 fl oz) water

Vanilla Syrup
4 tablespoons sugar
400 mL (13 fl oz) water
1 teaspoon vanilla essence (extract)

Place the soy powder and water in a deep saucepan over a high heat. Stir to dissolve, then continue stirring until the mixture comes to the boil. Simmer for 3 minutes.

Have a clean, dry 8–16 cup (2–4 litre, 3¼–6½ imp. pint) heatproof ceramic dish or 6 small serving bowls ready.

Add the packet of glucono delta lactone to the boiling soy mixture. Mix quickly with one stir of a whisk.

Quickly pour the soy mixture into the dish or dessert bowls, and allow the mixture to set without disturbing it further. If using small serving bowls, pour about ⅔–¾ cup (150–185 mL, 5–6 fl oz) mls of the mixture into each bowl and allow to set. Cover with a clean cloth.

To make the vanilla syrup, place the sugar and water in a saucepan. Bring to the boil, stirring occasionally so that the sugar dissolves, and allow to simmer for a few minutes for a rich flavour. Remove from the heat and add the vanilla essence. Allow to cool.

When the soy curd has set, serve with a little (about 60mL, 2oz) Vanilla Syrup drizzled over each serving.

SERVES 6

ASIAN SCREW-PINE AND GINGER SYRUP
This syrup is an alternative to the Vanilla Syrup. Place 4 tablespoons sugar, 400 mL (13 fl oz) water, 2–3 screw-pine leaves and 3–4 slices fresh ginger in a saucepan. Bring to the boil, stirring occasionally, and allow to simmer for a few minutes to develop the flavour. Remove from the heat

and allow to cool before serving with the soy curd.

Note: The Asian screw-pine is sometimes known as pandan. The leaves are commonly used is Asia and parts of Australia for flavouring sweet dishes. Pandan essence is available but is inferior to the green leaves.

BEANCURD BARLEY DESSERT

Cal : 964   kJ : 4049   Chol : 0 mg   Ca : 91mg

100 g (3$^1/_2$ oz) dried beancurd sheets (sweet variety)
$^1/_2$ cup (100 g, 3$^1/_2$ oz) pearl barley, rinsed and drained
6 cups (1.5 litres, 2$^1/_2$ imp. pints) cold water
1 can ginkgo nuts, about 100 g (3$^1/_2$ oz), drained and rinsed thoroughly
1 teaspoon vanilla essence (extract) or 3 screw-pine leaves
6 tablespoons sugar

Soak the bean curd sheets in warm water. Strain and place the sheets in a deep saucepan with the cold water.

Add the pearl barley and bring to the boil. Lower the heat to a simmer, cover and cook for 1$^1/_2$–2 hours.

Using a pointed knife, open the ginkgo nuts and remove the shoot in the middle of the nut (if left, the nut will taste bitter).

Add ginkgo nuts to the pan and contine to simmer, uncovered, for a further 20 minutes. If wished, add the vanilla extract or the screw-pine leaves, but not both.

Add the sugar and stir through to dissolve. Serve hot or lukewarm.
SERVES 6

Both barley and beancurd are rich in phytoestrogens. Ginkgo nuts can be purchased in can or in the shell. They are known as 'white nuts' in Asia. If using fresh gingko nuts, the white shells have to be cracked with a nut cracker before extracting the nut, which is rather juicy. Discard any dried-up nuts. The brown covering of the nut also has to be removed before it is added to the bean curd mixture.

SOY AGAR-AGAR

Cal : 656   KJ : 2652   Chol : 0 mg   Ca : 567 mg

$1^2/_3$ cups (400 mL, 13 fl oz) water
1 x 7 g ($^1/_4$ oz) packet agar-agar powder
2 cups (500 mL, 16 fl oz) soy milk
4 tablespoons sugar
4 tablespoons coconut milk powder

Pour $1^1/_3$ cups (350 mL, 11 fl oz) of the water into a deep saucepan. Add the agar-agar powder and stir well.

Bring the mixture to the boil, then add the soy milk and sugar.

Dissolve the coconut powder in the remaining water. Add this to the agar-agar mixture and bring to the boil once more.

Set in a deep rectangular ceramic or heatproof dish. Allow to cool, then refrigerate until set.

Cut the dessert into squares before serving with longans, lychees or halved strawberries.

SERVES 6–8

Agar-agar powder is made from seaweeds and contains natural fibre and iodine.It is available in blocks and strands, as well as in powdered form. However, if using strands, the consistency of the final product will vary slightly as it is difficult to titrate the amount of strands accurately to a standard amount of water. Also, sometimes the strands do not dissolve well during cooking so that the cooked liquid has to be strained before being allowed to set.

STRAWBERRY SOY DESSERT

Cal : 292   kJ : 1190   Chol : 0 mg   Ca : 264 mg

1 scant cup (200 mL, 7 fl oz) soy milk
150 g (5 oz) strawberries, rinsed, hulled and halved
4 teaspoons sugar or sweetener
2 teaspoons Nestle's Strawberry Quik or other strawberry-flavoured powdered milk
2 teaspoons powdered gelatine
1/4 cup (60 mL, 2 fl oz) hot water

Pour the soy milk into a blender and add the strawberries.

Add the sugar and Strawberry Quik, and blend for 30 seconds.

Dissolve the gelatine in the hot water in a saucepan.

Add the contents of the blender to the saucepan when the gelatine has dissolved completely. Stir thoroughly.

Pour the soy milk mixture into 2 dessert bowls and allow to set in the refrigerator.

SERVES 2

Gelatine has a high protein content.
Most strawberries are slightly sour in taste, and therefore need more sweetening than other fruits.

SOY APPLE CAKE

Cal : 2468   kJ : 10 167   Chol : 225 mg   Ca : 384 mg

4 medium green apples
$1/2$ cup (125 g, 4 oz) sugar
1 teaspoon ground cinnamon
4 cloves
$1/2$ cup (60 g, 2 oz) self-raising flour
$1/2$ cup (40 g, $1 1/2$ oz) soy flour
$1/4$ teaspoon bicarbonate of soda
$1/4$ teaspoon baking powder
scant $1/2$ cup (100 mL, $3 1/2$ fl oz) soy or canola oil
1 egg
scant $2/3$ cup (140 m, 5 fl oz) soy milk
$1/3$ cup (30 g, 1 oz) desiccated (shredded) coconut

Preheat the oven to 160°C (325°F). Grease a deep, round 20–25 cm (8–10 in) cake pan.

Peel the apples and cut into thin slices. Add 1 tablespoon of the sugar, cinnamon and cloves, and cook for 4 minutes in a microwave oven. Set aside to cool.

Sift the self-raising flour, soy flour, bicarbonate of soda and baking powder together.

Beat the remaining sugar, oil and egg together in a separate bowl. Add the sifted flours and fold through well, then add the soy milk and stir until the batter is smooth.

Pour the cooled apple into the bottom of the cake pan. Pick out the cloves and discard. Cover the apples with the cake batter and sprinkle the coconut evenly over the top.

Bake in the oven for 50–60 minutes, or until a skewer inserted into the centre of the cake comes out clean.

Cut the cake into 8 wedges while still in the pan and serve warm.
SERVES 4–8

This recipe uses ingredients high in phytoestrogens and is extremely delicious. Canned cherries or seeded prunes can be used instead of fresh apples.

APPLE MUFFINS

Cal : 2201   kJ : 9061   Chol : 525 mg   Ca : 623 mg

200 g (7 oz) apples, peeled and diced
3/4 cup (125 g, 4 oz) soft brown sugar
1 tablespoon honey
scant 1/3 cup (80 mL, 123/4 fl oz) canola oil
2 eggs, beaten
1/2 cup (40 g, 11/2 oz) soy flour
1 cup (125 g, 4 fl oz) wholemeal self-raising flour
1/2 teaspoon baking powder
2/3 cup (150 mL, 5 fl oz) soy milk
2 teaspoons ground cinnamon

Preheat the oven to 180°–190°C (350°–375°F). Grease two muffin pans.

Cook the apple in a microwave oven for 4 minutes. Set aside to cool.

Mix the brown sugar, honey and oil together in a mixing bowl. Add the eggs and mix well.

Sift the soy flour, wholemeal flour and baking powder into the bowl and combine thoroughly.

Gradually mix in the soy milk and cinnamon. When the batter is smooth, fold in the cooled apples.

Spoon the batter into the prepared muffin pans and bake in the oven for 17–20 minutes, or until a metal skewer inserted in the centre of a muffin comes out clean.

Allow the muffins to cool in the pan for a few minutes before turning out onto a wire rack.

MAKES 10–12 LARGE MUFFINS OR 28–30 SMALL MUFFINS

Eggs can be omitted from this recipe and extra soy milk used in their place. Use 1 tablespoon soy milk for each substituted egg. The honey and soy flour give these muffins a very moist texture. Do not be alarmed if the batter smells a little strange, as this is due to the soy flour. The smell will disappear during the cooking process.

GLOSSARY

Alzheimer's disease A degenerative condition affecting the brain leading to dementia.

Anti-angiogenic Ability to prevent new blood vessels from forming, especially in a tumour as rapidly growing tumours require a lot of nutrients for expansion and growth of the deviant cells. The nutrients are carried by the blood vessels. Thus by stopping more blood vessels from growing around the tumour sites, the growth of the tumour will be controlled.

Antibacterial Ability to fight against germs.

Anticoagulant A substance that has the ability to thin or dissolve blood clots.

Antifungal Ability to fight against fungus. A fungus belongs to the plant kingdom. An example of a fungus is candida.

Antihypertensive Ability to control or lower the blood pressure.

Anti-inflammatory Ability to suppress or soothe the inflamed parts of the body.

Anti-estrogenic Ability to oppose the effects of estrogens.

Antioxidants Chemicals that have the ability to prevent oxidation of food products. In the human body, these chemicals work to prevent free oxygen radicals from harming the body, e.g. formation of cholesterol plaques within the blood vessels. Examples of common antioxidants are vitamins C and E.

Antiviral	Ability to fight against viruses. An example of a virus is the common cold virus.
Benign	Not nasty in character. In medicine, usually used in reference to the nature of tumours.
Carotenemia	Excessive carotene in the body due to over-consumption of carotene-containing foods. Usually manifests itself by an orange–yellow skin; most evident on the palms of the hands.
Cholesterol	A component of fats in the body. This can come from the foods we eat or it can be manufactured in our liver. Cholesterol is usually divided into low density lipoproteins (LDL), very low density lipoproteins (VLDL) and high density lipoproteins (HDL). Much attention has been focused on the LDL cholesterol, as high levels of LDL are associated with increased risk of heart disease and hardening of the arteries.
Coumestans	Chemicals that are structurally related to isoflavones and have estrogenic effects. These are found in plant products such as alfalfa, clover, soybean sprouts and other legume sprouts.
DVT	Deep venous thrombosis. This refers to clots in the deep veins inside the legs.
Estradiol	The female hormone found in the blood of premenopausal women.
Estriol	The female hormone found in the blood of pregnant women.
Estrone	The female hormone found in the blood of menopausal women.

Fibroids   Benign fleshy growths in the uterus (womb) which can cause problems with periods.

Fluid retention   Feeling puffy in the legs and fingers, and often accompanied by a bloated tummy. This can be due to a number of causes. Women notice this problem around the time when they expect their periods to arrive.

Gastrointestinal Refers to the stomach, small bowel and large bowel.

Genistein   A chemical found in soy which has very strong estrogenic effects compared to the other plant estrogens. It has a strong anti-cancer effect on the body.

HRT   Hormone replacement therapy. This refers to the giving of hormones to humans in the treatment of a deficiency state. In this context, it refers to estrogens either alone or given in combination with a progesterone.

Isoflavones   Compounds found in some plant products which have estrogenic properties. These compounds are slightly different from those of coumestans in their structure. Genistein and daidzein are examples of the isoflavones.

Menopause   Refers to the last natural period. For most women, it is a retrospective label. A woman is said to have gone through menopause if she has not had a period in the preceding 12 months. If she is still having a period every 3 to 4 months, or even every 6 months, she has not yet reached menopause.

Menses   The monthly period.

Metabolism	The burning up of energy to keep the cells functioning.
Nausea	A feeling of sickness in the stomach or belly, causing one to have an urge to throw up the stomach contents.
Osteoporosis	The thinning of bone with loss of bone mineral density which can result in easy fractures with or without minimal trauma.
Pap smear	The sampling of cells from the cervix (mouth of the womb) for the detection of early cervical cancer.
Peri-menopause	The years immediately before the time of menopause. The peri-menopausal woman may experience irregularity in her periods, accompanied by some menopausal symptoms such as hot flushes, mood changes and sleeplessness.
Phytic acid	A chemical present in some plant products which can chelate metals such as zinc, calcium, iron etc. If ingested in large quantities, a person may experience cramps at night.
Phytoestrogens	Naturally occurring compounds found in some plants with estrogenic properties. These estrogens are similar in structure to human estrogens, but are very weak in their effects compared to the human ones.
Pre-menopause	The years of a woman's life before the change.
Progesterone	The other female hormone produced by the ovaries. In general, progesterone has anti-estrogenic effects.

Protease inhibitor   A chemical that blocks the action of specific enzymes thought to be responsible in the formation or growth of tumours.

Tempeh   A fermented soybean product which has a meaty and nutty taste. It is rich in proteins, iron, calcium and B group vitamins.

Tofu   Soybean curd made from concentrated soy milk with a coagulant added to set the mixture. Tofu is not as concentrated in nutrients as tempeh weight for weight.

Transit time   The time taken for the passage of a food item. In this context, refers to the time the food sub stance takes to pass through the digestive system.

REFERENCES

Adlercreutz H., et al. Dietary phyto-oestrogens and the menopause in
    Japan. Lancet 1992; 339: 1233

Adlercreutz H. Phytoestrogens from biochemistry to prevention of cancer
    and other diseases. Eighth International Congress on the
    Menopause Symposium 1996

Anderson, et al. Meta-analysis of the effects of soy protein intake on
    serum lipids. New Eng Jour. Med. 1995; 333: 276–282

Black C. Menopause: the alternative way. Aust Women Research Centre
    1994; No.1: 62–80

Bungay T., et al. Study of symptoms in middle life with special reference
    to the menopause. Br Med J. 1980; 281: 181–183

Carper J. Food: Your Miracle Medicine. HarperCollins 1993

Cashel K., English R., Lewis J. Composition of Foods, Australia. Aust Govt.
    Publishing Service 1989

Dennerstein L., et al. Menopausal symptoms in Australian women. Med J.
    Aust 1993; 159: 232–236

Dalais F. S. et al. The effects of phytoestrogens in postmenopausal
    women. Eighth International Congress on the Menopause
    Symposium 1996

Eden J. A., et al. A controlled trial of isoflavones for menopausal
    symptoms. Eighth International Congress on the Menopause
    Symposium 1996

Eden J. A. Oestrogen and the breast. 2. The management of the
    menopausal woman with breast cancer. Med J Aust 1992; 157:
    247–249

Edington R. F., et al. Clonidine (Dixarit) for menopausal flushing. CMA
    Jour. 1980; 123: 23–26

Griffiths K. Epidemiology of phytoestrogens, cancer and other diseases.
    Eighth International Congress on the Menopause Symposium
    1996

Hughes C. J. Phytoestrogens. Eighth International Congress on the
    Menopause Symposium 1996

Knight D. C., Eden J. Phytoestrogens: a short review, Maturitus 1995; 22:
    167–175

Lee H. P., et al. Dietary effects on breast-cancer risks in Singapore. Lancet 1991; 337: 1197–1200

Llewellyn-Jones D., Abrahams S. Menopause. Ashwood House/Penguin Books 1988: 65–75

Little B. The Complete Book of Herbs and Spices. Reed Books 1986

Murkies A. L., et al. Dietary flour supplementation decreases post menopausal hot flushes: effect of soy and wheat. Maturitus 1995; 21: 189–195

National Health and Medical Research Council. Dietary Guidelines for Australians. Aust Govt. Publishing Service 1992

Prince R. The calcium controversy revisited: implications of new data. Med J Aust 1993; 159: 404–406

Riggs B. L., Melton I. J. The prevention and treatment of osteoporosis. New Eng J Med 1992; 327: 9: 602–627

Saltman D. In Transition: A Guide to Menopause. Choice Books 1994

Stanton R. Complete Book of Food and Nutrition. Simon & Schuster 1989

Stuart M. The Colour Dictionary of Herbs and Herbalism. Orbis Publishing 1982

Van Schaick S. Symptomatic treatment of hot flushes. Ther. Update 1993: 61–65

Vines G. Cancer: is soy the solution? New Scientist 1994: July 14–15

Wilcox G. Effect of soy on menopausal symptoms. Eighth International Congress on the Menopause Symposium 1996

Wilcox G., et al. Oestrogenic effects of plant foods in post menopausal women. BMJ 1990; 30: 905–906

INDEX

PHOTOGRAPHS

OF

SOY PRODUCTS

Key:

1	savoury beancurd sheets (yuba)
2	soybeans
3	soybeans in tomato sauce
4	soyaroni pasta
5	soy beancurd sticks (yuba)
6	lethicin granules
7	tofu dessert
8	tofu cutlet
9	tempeh
10	fermented yellow soy beancurd cubes
11	soybean shoots
12	fermented red soy beancurd cubes
13	fried tofu strips
14	soy grits
15	sweet beancurd sheets (yuba)
16	soy flour
17	silken tofu
18	deep-fried tofu cubes, or tofu buk

Note: The brands pictured are examples only. There are many different brands of soy products on the market — try each of them to determine your favourite.

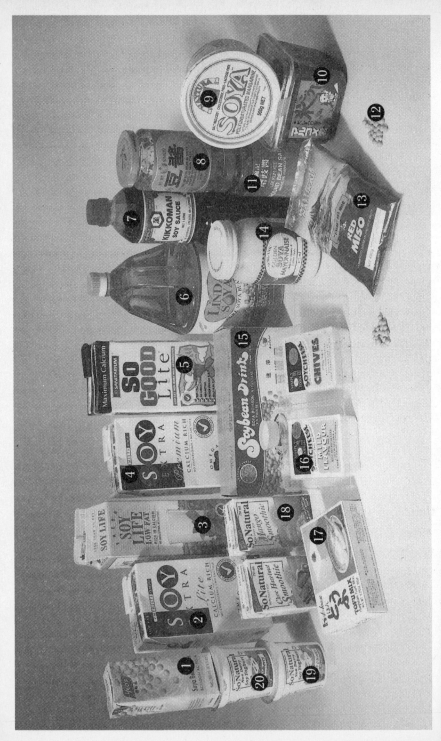

KEY:

1	UHT soy milk
2	low-fat calcium-enriched soy
3	fresh soy milk
4	calcium enriched soy milk
5	low-fat soy milk
6	soybean oil
7	soy sauce
8	fermented soybeans
9	soy margarine
10	miso with bonito, sake and seawood extracts
11	soybean paste, or ground bean sauce
12	soybeans
13	red miso paste
14	soy mayonnaise
15	soybean drink
16	soy cheese
17	tofu mix
18	soy smoothie
19	soy yoghurt
20	soy yoghurt

Note: The brands pictured are examples only. There are many different brands of soy products on the market — try each of them to determine your favourite.